Spirit of Steam

Further Adventures with Men of Steam

by

Raymond Flint

Santona Publications
Hull

Cover Design
from an Original Watercolour

Sandsend Arrival
by Adrian P Thompson
Hull

Also by the same author
The People's Scenario 1982
The March of the History Animal 1985
Men of Steam 1994
Head of Steam 1995
Power of Steam 1996

British Library Cataloguing-in-Publication data.
A catalogue record for this book is available from the British Library

First Published in 1998 by;
Santona Publications
Rydal Mount
224 Marlborough Avenue
Hull HU5 3LE.

Design and typesetting by Santona Publications.
Printed by The Amadeus Press Huddersfield.

ISBN 0 9507960 5 0

Acknowledgements

When I first completed 'Men of Steam' some years ago, I never imagined that the theme would stretch to a fourth volume. However, it has been due the encouragement of the many people whom I have had the pleasure of meeting, that Spirit of Steam has been written.

The support and assistance of my wife and family, friends and fellow Parkinsons' disease sufferers has been central to my achievement this far. But it is to a wider audience that I must turn to thank and acknowledge for inspiration and encouragement.

Firstly, those men and women of Scarborough's Railways who worked alongside me in the 1940s and 1950s, some of whom recognise themselves in the stories. It is perhaps their contribution to the enrichment of my life that has been a major source of inspiration.

Secondly, to all those who work amongst the many railway societies and preservation organisations that have brought me back to my roots through their own modern-day contributions to the age of steam. In particular those members and volunteers of organisations such as the North Eastern Railway Association, Friends of the National Railway Museum, The North Yorkshire Moors Railway, and the Severn Valley Railway.

Finally, to all those people who share the interest and enjoyment that steam railways bring to our lives.

Without all of these people this book, and those volumes which preceded it, may never have been written.

The Spirit of Santona
Onward to the Horizon

Santona Publications
Hull

Preface

Spirit of Steam is my fourth volume in the Men of Steam series of railway books which bring alive, through narrative, the experience of working on our steam railways in the 1940s.

Spirit of Steam, like its predecessors, is not a scholarly or academic historical study of the railway and its trains, but a dramatised account of life on our steam railways and the footplate. Many of the events and characters portrayed in the book are based on true life, some have been embellished to provide amusement and humour, but all reflect the daily hopes, struggles, worries and comradeship that steam railway men and women witnessed at this time in our history.

The steam locomotives which are cast in a central role in these stories were both loved and revered and cursed and hated by the men who worked on them. Today the way of life is just a memory, but the heritage lives on. Since the early days of Watt, Trevithick and Stephenson, the steam engine was a key factor in our industrial and economic development, powering the locomotives on our railways, the ships on the high seas and the machines in our factories.

Indeed the steam engine is an important part of our history, but it is its use in powering the railway locomotive that above all captures the magic for everyone. It is thanks to the generous efforts of thousands of volunteers and benefactors that our steam railway heritage survives today within the many preservation schemes, large and small, up and down the country.

There are over than 400 miles of track on more than 100 preserved lines, creating an annual turnover of over £40m and carrying more than 8 million passengers a year.

It is now 30 years since the steam locomotive ended its time on our national railways. Dieselisation and electrification were inevitable in the economic atmosphere of the 1960s. But the age of steam is not yet dead. As long as the empowered preservation movement continues with its sterling efforts, the age of steam will not close or fade away, it will continue to bring to men, women and children that unique magic and wonder that only the steam railway locomotive can evoke.

I hope too that this book, in its own small way, will contribute to keeping that magic alive for all time.

Ray Flint
11th August 1998

SPIRIT OF STEAM

CONTENTS

1
Mutual Improvement

The Winter sunshine pierced the sooty glass panels of the station roof and dappled the empty platforms with a patchwork of light and shadow. It was a cold and clear Sunday morning in early January. Not the sort of day you would expect to find sixteen loco men dressed in clean overalls and seated inside Castlebrough Station waiting-room.

They were participating, if somewhat boisterously, in the shedman's Mutual Improvement Class. The young locomotive cleaners and those passed as locomotive firemen always made it a relaxed social occasion, but, in spite of their constant laughter and chaffing, they were serious about learning.

"It's good that the railways are being nationalised," Jim Simpson said to the chairman of the class as he placed a large track diagram on the tripod blackboard.

"That's politics," interrupted Arthur Wilko sharply, "and this isn't a politics class. Keep on the subject." The middle-aged driver enjoyed having a dig at Jim Simpson and his politics. "We're 'ere for learning about railway rules and reg's."

"Yes I know," Jim replied to Arthur. "It is politics," he emphasised, "but it's our job. The Transport Bill is going through Parliament now. It's expected to be law by forty-seven."

"The L.N.E.R.'s finished then? Thank the Lord for that. Amen. Amen." Willie Wagget said with mock joy in his voice.

"It's not going to do anything for you lads," Arthur answered, more as the devil's advocate and out of opposing Jim Simpson for the fun of it.

"What do yuh want, Willie? To continue as L.N.E.R."

"Phew, I'm fed up with cleaning engines. I want to do more firing."

"You'll get more work when we're nationalised, more than we get on the L.N.E.R." Arthur Coleford contributed this seemingly knowledgeable response, digging Joe in the ribs and adding, "Eh?"

"We'll still be run by the same gaffers that's for sure," added Hibbo.

"Let's get on and leave the politics to the old men," skitted Joe making his first contribution.

"Oh, he's not asleep," Arthur Coleford said with a grin and added. "Thought you'd gone home Joe, you're unusually quiet."

"A lot of money is necessary to build up the railways. I think the Government is the only one with enough money." Town Councillor Jim Simpson was preparing, together with his colleague Harry Busby, to act as instructors to Castlebrough Mutual Improvement Class.

"No politics here Councillor," chirped Arthur Wilko again.

"He thinks he's teachin' economics for the N.C.L.C.," added the noisy Hibbo.

"He thinks! he's not thinking at all," Bob Burton answered with emphasis, then addressed himself to Wagget and Hibson. "If he was, he wouldn't have you two jokers in."

"A good pack of cards has two jokers," replied Wagget smugly.

"Just for Willy and Hibbo I've written a bit of poetry," said Simpson regaining authority. "It's not quite as good as Robbie Burns," he smiled knowingly at Wagget and Hibson who were due to take their fireman's tests on the following Wednesday. "But it's got a good bit o' Yorkshire dialect in it."

He draped a piece of wallpaper over the blackboard. The poetry was clearly displayed. He read it aloud with emphasis, rhythm and Yorkshire dialect.

Look for t'Guard, his whistle an' 'is flag,
See all the boards's off, front and back,
Nay blowing off, no camel's humps nor black smoke,
Keep a bright fire, full glass and steady stoke.

You've got to gather in t'coal,
and feed it in t'fire 'ole,
Keep the footplate tidy an' be alert all the time,
Keep a steady head o'steam an' don't mek her prime,
Sure enough, if yuh's done yuh bit,
and kept a lid on yuh cheek an' wit,
yuh fireman's tests yuh'll be sure to pass,
In a flash, wi' marks first class.

Applause and laughter showed the appreciation of the full class. Hibson, who felt slightly humiliated at the fact that he was the subject of the joke, asked of Simpson. "Why is their such interest in Robbie Burns amongst railwaymen. I've heard a few that say lines from Burns."

"I'm glad you asked that," said the shedmaster, Mr Franker, from the back of the group. He had quietly slipped in to join them without being noticed. The recognition of the Franker's voice subdued the men into a hush, they sat in anticipation of his next comment. "I visited the A.S.L.E.F. library in London. I'd always wondered myself why Robert Burns' poems were popular with Locomotivemen. One reason might be to do with the first Rule Book of the Society in eighteen eighty-one. The two verses of Burns' poem, 'Man was made to mourn' are the first words of the first rule book of the loco man's union. A tough honest statement of the engineman as an independent soul. Whilst he could be dismissed instantly, he'd never, grovel or lick any boots."

"Aye, quite right too." Wagget added innocently hoping he would not be hounded for his remark of insolence.

"And they're still the same awkward lot today," Franker added firmly aiming his comment in Wagget's direction. "Listen," he commanded and he read out aloud with a passion and conviction that riveted the eyes of his audience upon himself.

If I'm yon haughty lordling's slave,
By Nature's Law designed,
Why was an independent wish,
E're planted in my mind?

If not why am I subject to,
His cruelty or scorn,
Or why has man the will and power,
To make his fellow Mourn.

Franker's rendition of Burns cast a sense of purpose upon the meeting. Joe looked around wondering what they would be all thinking about. The group settled and got down to some serious discussion which Jim Simpson managed to spin out for a good two hours.

"Time for some refreshment," announced Willy Wagget as the class dispersed and some of them prepared themselves for a visit to the Pavilion Vaults or the Railway Tavern.

"Do you know of any other group of workers who go to work on a Sunday morning without pay?" asked Joe, "and teach themselves."

"Are we the crackers, or what?" asked Willie Wagget as they crossed from the station to the Pavilion Hotel. "We don't even have a classroom at our shed. At Hull, Springhead shed, I think it is, they have a classroom, with moving models, y'know working models of locomotives an' things."

Jim Simpson nodded agreement and called across to Hibbo and Alf South as they departed. "Hope you two pass your tests good luck."

"Me too," added Joe. "Remember, little and often, no camel's humps and keep yuh peeper's open."

Politics was still a popular subject of discussion at work that week.

"It's called Keynesianism," Fifty Bob Burton conveyed knowledge-ably to Joe across the cab. "But it's just another fancy name for govern-ment intervention."

He and Joe were busy shunting Castlebrough's Washbeck coal yard. Fifty Bob was explaining the meaning of Keynesianism to an interested Joe. Their discussion took place as they worked their saddletank W.D. locomotive number 8017 up and down the yard moving wagons to and fro. Joe's attention drifted away from the debate as he watched the yard shunter, Bert Beer, controlling and stopping the loose running wagons with a skilled flick on the hand brakes.

"It looks hard work for Bert running up and down a big coalyard, cou-pling and uncoupling, hundreds of wagons. He must get worn-out."

"Yeh," Fifty Bob replied. "It's a hard job shunting loose wagons for hours. It'll keep him fit though."

Shunter Bert checked his wagons were securely braked and then ran to join the W.D. tank that had diverted to another part of the yard. "Have your breakfast now lads," he called out.

"Stay put here, Bob," said Joe, who'd seen the shunter's hand signals and heard the word breakfast. "He said stay here until he comes back. He's got four fingers up and pointing across the road. He's lookin' at a piece of paper an' holdin' it up."

Bob peered out of the cab towards Bert. "I know what he wants," Fifty Bob exclaimed as he screwed down the locomotive handbrake. "Joe, go and get me four hot bread rolls from Mac's bakery shop. Two for Bert, an' two for us, oh, an get us a Daily Mirror."

"You understood all that sign language?" questioned Joe. Bob nodded. "There's a lot of sign language here on the railways," Joe continued. "All the hand signal codes in the rule book, but there's a lot more isn't there?"

Bob was now slightly sarcastic. "Yeh, that's rest, that's eat, that's go away," he demonstrated with his hands. "And this," he said nipping his nose between finger and thumb and pulling the imaginary lavatory chain with his free hand. "Means you're a crap-house."

They both laughed. Bob had a final word. "On the footplate there's a lot of sign language between the crew. Somebody'll probably write a book on it one day."

With Joe back from the bakery, Bert joined them in the cab. They ate their sandwiches and bread cakes whilst Bert told how he'd heard that the eighteen mile single branch line to Pickering was soon to be re-laid and that there was a plan to build a station at Butlins Holiday Camp near Filey. "That's going to be Government money and planning."

"It's nearly a year since the War finished, will be in a couple of months," responded Joe slowly and thoughtfully. "There's still a lot of unemployment. You say the Government's going to do more. I hope so, I'm next but one to be made up to fireman. There are lots of jobs advertised at Hull and York. Sutton's going, so is Dabb, Johnny Marsay's next in line above me, though he's not leaving."

"You won't have long to wait," added Bert. "There're lots of big developments under way. Three new platforms to be built at the station. Londesborough Road excursion station is going to re-open too. You could be driving within three or four years."

"That's my dream, my steam dream," commented Joe. "One day I might work on the 'Flyer' all the way to London from Castlebrough and I might drive it."

"You dream son," said Bob with a hint of caution. "But remember Robbie Burns' line, 'The plans of mice and men go oft awry'. Yuh know," he paused thoughtfully. "That's what I think'll happen to this new Keynesianism. Guaranteed full employment. I ask you?"

"An' as they say," added Joe. "Pigs might fly."

"That's right. Don't count yuh chickens," said Bert. "Exciting times though, full-employment for all them that's fit enough, that's a big promise."

"Being on the railways is a bit like being at school. There's always someone to teach you something, or books to read." Joe gabbled on.

"Life's your school now, you'll learn a lot more from that than any school'll teach yuh."

Two blasts on a distant whistle called them back to work and shunting recommenced. Joe's dreams of promotion and learning went on whilst the W.D. shunting engine shuffled the wagons about the yard.

Their conversation topic continued as they shunted the yard, or travelled to other parts of Castlebrough taking Bert with them in the cab. "The working week is still forty-eight hours plus overtime. It's been like that for twenty-five damned years or more." Fifty Bob complained. "We might get the forty-four hour week before too long. Only just got two week's annual holiday a year ago."

"Things 'ave got to change," said Bert Beer. "Think what the Yanks get, holidays and pensions, and good living as well."

"We should have a pension. White collar workers are pensioned. We get nowt, nowt to write home about. No sick pay." Fifty Bob related his despondency of the present system and Joe felt his own contribution was overdue.

"What about Sunday pay. It ought to be double time at least. An' the two week's holiday was long overdue."

"Yuh can say that again," Bob grumbled."I didn't have time to get washed and get me suit on when we only had a weeks holiday. It was time to go back to work before I'd stopped spitting coal dust and soot."

The six-wheeled 8017 coasted from the station coal cells towards Gasworks Up Sidings and was signalled to cross over the number one 'Independent' line towards the shed yard.

"What's the Washbeck cabin signalman waving us to stop for?" asked Joe.

"Oh, he'll have got some stuff for me, sprouts an' apples," stated Fifty Bob, "I said I'd pick 'em up and take 'em home on the engine. I'd almost forgotten."

They halted alongside the long two-storied wood and glass signal cabin. The bag of produce was passed across from the signal cabin's observation platform with the remark, "I've written the prices down, for you, Bob. I'll see you tomorrow about settling up."

"Thanks. My mate'll carry them home for me."

"Have you heard the news." asked the signalman. " There's been a nasty rail smash in the early hours. Nine people killed and 12 injured but they haven't got everybody out yet. It's on the radio. About five this morning it happened."

"Where abouts?" queried Fifty Bob.

"Near Durham, Ferryhill, somewhere around there."

"There was train smash only t'other day, wasn't there?" Bob responded with a thoughtful enquiry.

The signalman on the cabin observation platform replied. "Aye, something like that was said on the wireless. A crash at Lichfield, and another one somewhere. That made three smashes, with dead on 'em all. All within a week."

"What's caused that?" asked Joe.

"Don't know, I've just heard about 'em same time as you."

The signalman added a bit more news, "The Home Secretary, Chuter Ede was on the train, escaped without serious injury though. The wireless reckoned it's all down to the state of the railways. Bad maintenance, everything worn out. That's what's causing all these crashes."

The telephone bell in the cabin rang and the signalman disappeared inside to answer it returning a few moments later with a new instruction.

"Yuh'll have to go, Bob there's an engine behind you waiting. I'm turning you into the shed, they want you to go to Sander with the toolvans. There's a wagon come off in the yard an its foulin' the main line."

"Crike. Could've done without that. See yuh later, thanks for this lot." Bob waved and soon had the saddle tank engine departing quickly.

"Any of that coming my way?" asked Joe, pointing hopefully at the bags of produce.

"Well, can yuh carry them up to our house for me whilst I report in about the Sander job. Then we'll sort something out."

"What we goin' in the shed yard for?" asked Joe.

"To stand down the shed side, there it won't be so far for you to carry the bags."

"The signalman said we had to go Sander."

"He said that, but I say I won't be going," said Fifty Bob. He ran the loco up the side road and stopped. Bob didn't go asking for instructions, he loaded the two bags of garden produce onto Joe's shoulders. "You've got five minutes whilst I sort out the Sander job. You know my house, it's only two minutes walk, leave them in the closet in the back garden. Here's the closet key, lock the door and shove the key through the letter box."

Joe quickly performed his un-rostered task and returned to the shed. Fifty Bob was missing when he got back to the saddletank loco. Passed Fireman Robert Cass was waiting in the cab for Joe. "Where've you been. Fifty Bob said you'd be back in a minute. Anyway it don't matter. Now you're here. As long as you keep awake. We're going to Sander."

"I thought Fifty Bob was going with me."

"Yuh must know he's in the local link and can't go on the mainline."

Joe knew of the local link. Specially reserved jobs for local men who were not fit enough to work trains on the main line or needed light or rehabilitating work. Those who were a bit less sophisticated or insensitive often mockingly called it the 'Sick Lame and Lazy Link'. Joe, through his own inexperience had earlier been humiliated by the nickname. He had displayed a letter in the notice case in the messroom announcing his candidature for election to the 'Local Departmental Committee'. He'd included a statement of his determination, if elected, to improve the type of work allocated to 'The Sick, Lame and Lazy link'. He cancelled his candidature at the first bitter attack by men in the Local Link, he'd foolishly thought that it was the correct title.

'After that,' Joe asked himself. 'How could I have forgotten that Fifty Bob couldn't go to Sander Station because of his health problem.' Passed Fireman Cass was promoted to driver for the day to relieve Fifty Bob.

"Are yuh fit and ready to go with the breakdown vans to Sander. Some wagons have been derailed by the Hull goods engine. The down line sidings are blocked."

"Yes, and they're stopped foul of the main line."

"So yuh know then, no need for me to tell yuh."

The breakdown vans, crewed by the fitter, his mate, two labourers and Franker the shedmaster, were alongside to get the line opened quickly. Because the wagons and the breakdown train were in the same block signalling section as the de-railed wagons the breakdown train was allowed to travel to the obstruction on the wrong line.

"D'yuh see what we've done? By coming this way," Bob asked of Joe.

"Not really, We could have come out on the other line and still got alongside surely."

"Yes but we would have stopped both lines," Bob explained. "This way Franker believes we can keep traffic running down one line with very little delay, whilst we pull the first wagon upright and on to the rails."

"But what if it falls the way which it's leaning and falls onto that mainline?"

"We'll try to make sure that it doesn't, or we'll have both mainlines blocked and may have to send for the steam crane."

"You think he knows what he's doing?"

"They say Franker is one of the best, he's had all sorts of jobs on the North Eastern. Very experienced," said Bob.

The four wagons had been full of coal when they were shunted into the coal cells, free-wheeling down the slope. They derailed at the points, the coal contents of two of the overturned privately-owned wagons were strewn all around, the other two wagons remained upright and full.

A hurried examination by Franker and the chief fitter from the loco shed started the action. Safety precautions were carefully checked, detonators put in position and the contents of the breakdown vans were quickly unloaded. The two labourers were set the initial task of shovelling up the scattered coal.

A full kettle was starting to bubble on a small primus stove alongside the track. "Important things first," said Bob, nodding his head in the direction of the tea. "Have you got any tea, Joe? I could do with a drink."

"I can't see how they are going to right them wagons without lifting gear. What do you think?" Joe asked.

"You just watch 'em. I've seen a loco on its side uprighted without a crane."

Anchor points and pulleys, chains, jacks, tools and ropes were assembled and attached to the saddle tank loco which heaved slowly forward. The pulleys and chains took the strain and the empty coal wagon rolled slowly over and settled its four wheels. Small jacks lifted the wagon higher, and timber and metal ramps quickly created a rough roadbed along which the upright wagon could be pulled until it fell neatly into position on the rails.

"That's one on. Only twenty minutes."

"And the tea's coming round. Wouldn't be surprised if a pack o' dominoes or dice appeared for a quick game. Give them twenty minutes and the next wagon will be on the rails."

"Not twenty minutes!"

"See that chap taking the first mug of tea. Well, I'll just bet you two-shillings that from him taking his first drink the second wagon will be on the lines and pushed clear into the yard in twenty minutes."

Joe placed his watch and his two shillings on the driver's seat and he and Bob counted the minutes as they ticked away. An identical procedure was followed the second wagon was soon pulled sideways up and over onto its wheels.

"Still six minutes to go," said Joe. "They only have to get it on the rails and push it clear into the coal yard and I've lost my two shillings. I reckon you knew a lot more about this game than you cracked on."

The engine hauled the wagon along another rough carpet of timber, packing, and ramps and back onto the rails within eighteen minutes. "You were right," Joe conceded to his driver.

"It's not finished yet," said Bob. "We said pushed clear into the yard. They won't push it back until the ganger checks the rails with his gauge."

The other two partly derailed wagons were clear of the mainline and well within the goods yard. Main line trains could now pass safely at slow speed in both directions without using single line operation.

"Twenty-one minutes I make it," said Bob. "You just won."

Franker suddenly climbed up the loco side and into the cab. "I've got to get back to the shed. Take me back Robert as soon as the road is clear. George, will take over from now on. You come back here as soon as you've dropped me at the shed. One of our men has been injured in a road accident . Got to get back. You'll be quicker than me booking a taxi."

"Joe come on, quick. Put light engine lamp code right."

Both Joe and Bob noticed a change in the temperament of Mr Franker. He had a look of concern, but didn't say anymore. As soon as the signal-man gave permission, they raced away from the sidings towards Castlebrough. Bob and Joe returned with their engine to Sander as soon as Franker had left.

Sander Station Master was at the end of the long island platform when they returned. He'd just come out of the signal cabin. Bob drew the W.D. saddle-tank engine to a halt alongside him and received the news of why they'd just taken the shedmaster back to Castlebrough.

"George, George Barlby. Had an accident, he's dead did you say?" Bob was repeating what the station master was telling him.

"No, they didn't say he was dead, someone said he was so badly injured he might be dead."

"What's happened," enquired Joe.

"Nobody knows. Looks as if he was cycling down Guzzet Hill and something jammed in his front wheel. Yuh know how fast you can come down that hill."

"George Barlby, head injuries, face pretty bad," said Bob, giving the details to Joe. "He'd laid for two hours before someone found him. He was due for the coal train so it would happen about five o'clock this morning. He was found at seven."

"Mister Franker always visits anyone hurt or injured at work," Bob explained to Joe.

"He's a good gaffer," answered Joe, who based his judgement on what was the almost universal consent of the men at the shed.

Their job at Sander had to be completed before the station goods yard could be functional again. Their task was soon completed and the rails made safe for traffic. Bob and Joe arrived back at Castlebrough in time for their relief to take over at one-thirty and continue shunting for a further seven hours.

"That was a good, quick job well done," said Bert Beer, their shunter. "Mister Franker doesn't play about. He chose the best course of action, that's clear."

Bob agreed, "No trains held for more than three minutes, and seven trains signalled through. Really they weren't even late."

"Really," said Joe. "I learnt quite a bit today, about railway operating and dealing with derailments, I mean."

"More lessons from the school of life, eh lad."

"Tosher! Tosher, Wade!" The voice belonged to Bill Clarke who was nearby and abruptly interrupted their chatting. "You're mate Fifty Bob, he's left a message for you, where's his bags of stuff. He can't find 'em."

Joe was puzzled. He'd taken them to Fifty Bob's house as instructed.

"I'll call and see him as I go home."

He arrived at the house, and knocked. He remembered the red painted door, but the person who answered was an elderly lady, completely unknown to him.

He explained he had left the bags, "For Mister Burton, an engine driver at the shed."

"There's one that lives at number six." she said. "What bags?"

Joe explained that he, Mister Burton's fireman, had delivered two bags and left them in the outside closet and put the key through the letterbox of this house.

"Oh! I know what wi' talkin' about now luvvy," answered the old lady. "Here's the key, there are two bags are in the privvy. This is the wrong house, luvvy, this is sixteen, not six, where that gentleman lives." The lady pointed to a chalk- marked number one on the door next to the brass number six. "The one's fallen off," she said.

An embarrassed but grateful Joe muttered his thanks to the kind neighbour and delivered his charge to number six without any further explanation. Bob Burton answered his knock on the door and grasped the bags off Joe. The unusual and serious accident which had befallen George Barlby completely preoccupied his mind. The shed Welfare Club collector was already collecting the standard call for George who would be without wages for a long time.

2
Under a Spell

"Who's he?" asked Joe, pointing to the name 'M. Spell' on the daily roster displayed in the messroom notice case. Joe and his two fellow railwaymen, Alf South and Arthur Coleford, stared through the glass at the sheet.

"He's the York driver whose been placed at our shed," Alf replied. "Hadn't yuh 'eard."

Passed Cleaner Coleford couldn't wait to add his own sombre forecast, "Your luck's run-out, Joe, he's a right misery guts they say."

"Don't put the poor beggar off, Arthur. You ain't bin wi' Spell. You're only repeating what somebody else has said."

Joe was still optimistic. "It's a nice little job for me, light engine to Darlington, 90 miles isn't it. Just my cup o' tea, then off for two days rest." He grinned at his colleagues as he spoke. "Glad I'm not in the shed on cleaning. I don't care who my mate is."

"I've not been with him Alf, and you haven't either," emphasised Coleford. He put a hand on Joe's shoulder. "It's only what we've heard. Maybe not to give a dog a bad name until it's bitten you."

"I'm only going to York and Darlington shops with an engine, I surely can't do anything to annoy him on a trip like that. I don't care if he's like King Kong."

Michael Spell was an engine driver from York Motive Power Department. He had been transferred to Castlebrough Shed for a limited period. As a York man, he knew 'the road' from York to Darlington well and was consequentially the only driver available to deliver a D49 locomotive to Darlington Railway workshops.

As a driver based at another shed, Spell, would not have been allowed by the Castlebrough crews and management to work as a driver without prior consultation and agreement. The L.N.E.R. Motive Power Superintendent had requested that Spell be given work at Castlebrough shed for an unspecified period. He did so without making the reason public knowledge. The Local Departmental Committee of men and management had agreed to the request and the confidentiality. No one, it appeared, knew why Spell had been allocated temporary work at Castlebrough.

Joe wandered slowly up number eight road where the D49 class locomotive awaited his attention. There was plenty of time, or so he thought. He had been allocated one hour to prepare the engine for the road. He walked casually up the path between the stationary locomotives whistling a sequence of notes that he graced with the title of popular tunes.

The sight of a tall, slim man oiling the right hand side-rods of engine number 2751 alerted him to the possibility that the stranger was likely to be his driver. "Hello" Joe shouted cheerfully through the gloom. Joe had no reason to worry about working with him.

"Are you the fireman?" The question was thrown sharply at Joe. He was about to respond but another question was presented. "What time do you call this?" The tone and attitude of the driver seemed to proclaim authority and demand immediate obedience. The man had a long face with a sharp forward jutting jaw. His skin looked as dry as parchment and his eyes peered hauntingly from within deep sockets. He didn't wait for Joe's reply and snapped out more questions. "What time do you think it is? What day is it?"

"Er, it's, er, just gone seven," Joe answered slowly. "Just gone seven."

"It's seven-thirteen, thirteen bloody minutes late, fourteen now." What time were you supposed to sign on, afternoon or morning." Joe was floored by the hostile and aggressive attitude of the driver whom he assumed to be Spell, he was slow to react.

"I said to you, what time do you call this, now, what's the time, now?"

Joe still paused, he was shell-shocked. The tall figure holding him on parade was almost too big and verbal for Joe to dominate. The man had the manner of a drill sergeant, and he did his best to look like one. The soft shiny top of his loco cap was stiffened with a circular card inserted within. It made the front stand upright and tight, giving it a military style.

"Well, what do I have to do to get an answer out of you?" Spell thrust his face close, glowering eyeball to eyeball. As he did, Joe caught sight of a circular, brass army badge on his cap and a military decoration on his jacket lapel. The man started bawling incomprehensibly and with such force that he sprayed Joe's face with a shower of saliva.

Joe put his hand up and pushed the objectionable man back, taking a moment to wipe an arm of his overall across his spattered face.

"Fifteen minutes past seven o'clock," replied Joe, markedly louder and clearly more irritated than previously.

"So you can talk. I was beginning to think that you was a dummy."

"I'm sorry," Joe started and paused, he played his discretion card. "I'm very sorry but my Mother is ill and I had something to do for her. She's left at home in bed, till someone comes home from work."

"Nurse-maiding your mammy at your age. Soldier? You, at Tobruk,

Sicily, El Alamein, Cyprus, or running from the Japs? Or are yuh a conchie."

Joe stepped backwards and stumbled onto a pile of hot clinker. Swayed by growing anger, he felt his hands tighten into fists. He swung his arm back ready to thrust out with a right hook. But his motion was arrested. Arthur Coleford's hand had grasped at his arm. He pulled at Joe's shoulder putting himself between Joe and Spell.

"Whoa kiddo! Cool it mate." Coleford instructed, pushing Joe along towards the loco cab steps. "Get into the cab Joe."

"You all right, Mr Spell?" Arthur asked.

Spell blurted out in defence. "He was telling me a mammby-pamby tale about bein' late, I nearly lost my temper. He was bloody well going to hit me, I saw it in his eyes."

"Joe Wade's alright, Mr Spell, but with him being a bit of a boxer he's fast to lose his rag."

"He'd better behave on the footplate, or I'll give him hell. I'll make a proper man of him. The young upstart. He'll wish he'd never arrived late for parade."

"Parade?" echoed Coleford enquiringly.

"Yes, work, parade, duty, he's got to learn some."

Wagget and Mason appeared nearby and the tense atmosphere calmed, almost as if their immediate presence had stirred feelings of guilt amongst the antagonists.

Joe worked silently in the engine cab. He calmed down a little more when Arthur Coleford joined him on the footplate and gave him some prudent advice. "You're on a cushy job today, be careful and keep quiet."

While they tidied the cab, Spell looked in through the doorway, "Make sure the cab's clean. I don't want it to look like a crap-house just because it's going to the shops."

"Aye," responded Joe, reacting in accordance with Arthur Coleford's well intentioned advice.

An uneasy quiet settled on Driver Spell and Joe progressed restlessly with his work. Spell displayed no further interest in Joe so he diligently cleaned and polished the boiler front and anything within his reach. 'Gleaming brasses,' thought Joe, 'might just calm the beast.'

Spell followed all the correct procedures. He checked on Joe's work without comment until he found something amiss. "There's only eleven detonators," he declared. "There should be twelve." Joe braced for another verbal attack but the little piece of tinder within the sullen driver only smouldered on.

After a few strained miles down the mainline towards York, Joe accepted that he was in for a miserable day. "Don't open that damper!" the driver snapped when Joe laid a hand on the damper handle. "We're going like the clappers now, I'm in a rush to get back." Spell continued to harry Joe. "You're making black smoke, there's no need for it. You don't need that injector on now. Where did you learn to fire a locomotive?" Only a few seconds followed that remark before Joe heard him add very loudly to himself, "I don't know where they go for the dregs they recruit as firemen these days."

Iron self-discipline fought with every aggressive impulse and emotion within Joe's body. Spell's blistering responses to any action undertaken by Joe provoked him to fight back, but Joe resisted all temptation. As they halted at a signal on the approach to York, Joe attempted to make conversation again.

"The weather's good for this time of year," he said timidly. He didn't get a reply but he felt less pessimistic now that he had spoken without anger. "This Year is going to be the first full year of peace since 1939."

"Is it?" came back an uncompromising reply.

They threaded their way through the relief lines at York and commenced journeying northwards towards Darlington at a reckless pace. Spell stepped across the cab to stand near Joe and keep an eye on the road through the spectacle window.

"You just get on with your duties son, don't prattle on. You'll be all right with me. If you just keep quiet. I've got a job to do."

"Yes," said the deflated but frustrated Joe. "I was only....., I can get on with anybody." But Spell's face remained motionless. 'God, how do I cope with this stuck up sod?' Joe talked to himself. 'What a miserable git.'

The miles swallowed the painful silence that Spell imposed on their relationship. Only engine sounds and passing trains kept the cab a noisy place where vocal expressions were outlawed.

When finally they were stopped at a signal on the approach to Darlington Joe tried again to be conciliatory. "How long do you think you'll be working at Castlebrough? York must be an exciting place to be alongside Castlebrough."

"That's my business. What do you want to know for?"

Joe smarted, he could hardly believe the sharpness of the man's response. "I was just chatting," he mumbled back.

"What? speak up damn you."

"I was just chatting," he repeated with a bit more spirit.

"Who's trying to get to know things about me? Who's told you to ask?" Spell now displayed an anger laced with venom.

"I'm sorry. I'm not prying," stuttered Joe. He had still to put on an act, to try and subdue the hostility and anger that was building up within him. He was trying hard not to lose his temper. He knew, if he lost his temper he would say things he would regret, but really he wanted to plant a 'bunch of fives' on Spell's nose. Anxiety overwhelmed him and he backed away from Spell to stand on the tender fall-plate and look out onto the railway approaches to Darlington Workshops.

"I know there's some at Castlebrough have got it in for me. God help you, if your one." Spell fumed. Joe could feel the man's presence close behind him. He feared that Spell might be about to be attack him, or push him from the moving locomotive.

A yard-man with shunting pole in hand grasped the loco handrail and joined them in the cab. His presence was welcomed by Joe. Now Spell's attention was diverted to driving the loco through the yard whilst the yard man leapt on and off to set the hand points and direct them towards their final destination.

Spell collected his belongings from the locker and instructed Joe with a curt, "Follow me." But before they'd even left the cab Joe faced another virulent verbal onslaught. "I'm in charge. Don't you bloody well forget. Just shut up and follow me."

"You are the Captain?" Joe responded to his torturer with complete submission but with a look that could kill and an acid tone in his voice which should have burnt his ears.

"I said shut up, can't you get the bloody message. I don't want to bloody well talk to you."

Exasperation flooded over Joe. "Why are you so flaming miserable?" he blurted at the menacing figure.

"Don't you bloody well talk to me like that. I could have you up on a charge at H.Q." Spell lunged forward threateningly and Joe thrust up the coal shovel in self defence.

"I'll smack you with this...," but his resolve faltered and the word 'shovel' fizzled out in his mind.

"Right, that's enough soldier." Spell spluttered his words out with a hail of saliva. "I'm going to do you a favour. I'll have you on report for insubordination and coming late."

"That's no favour," muttered Joe giving way to fear and caution and turning to leave the engine cab.

"You can go and find a bloody job where they let you gabble your head off." Joe didn't reply. "If I get wind that you've talked too anybody about me. I'll have you on the carpet at York so fast you'll think your backside's alight."

Joe remained silent. Spell left the cab of the D49 with Joe following at a discreet distance, walking towards the time office. With a curt, "Wait here for me!" Spell vanished down a corridor

'He must need the lavatory' Joe thought. 'He'll have to go to the time office as well.' He sighed with relief. For a moment he relaxed but then horror struck. 'Crike, maybe he's going to report me now.' The thought troubled him immensely and quickly he resolved on action.

He started to run down a corridor, as if to escape, but found himself in the Fitters' Shop. He sped through the shop, past the Smith's coke furnace which was host to glowing irons. He ran through a door and into a long workshop. Then on, between ranks of locomotives and startled men. He leapt over engineering materials and brushed hard against a pair of young apprentices causing them to drop their heavy load with a loud metallic clang. On with urgency, on and then out into the daylight.

Despite his heavy boots and overalls, he sped on at a rate that surprised him. No one stopped him or called out. He only slowed when he was aside the running lines again with Darlington station in his sights.

Back at the station he took refuge in the buffet and reflected on his impulsive action with an uneasy realisation. 'I'll get next train to Middlesbrough then on to Whitby and the coast road,' he deliberated with himself. 'Spell won't go that way, surely. I don't ever want to see that long, lean, mean, face of his ever again.'

It took another four hours for him to return to Castlebrough via his chosen route. The sun was low in the late afternoon sky as he walked from the station to Castlebrough shed. His route took him down number four road directly towards the store. He could hear Chargeman Bill Clarke's voice echoing from within. It wasn't Clarke's voice that stopped Joe. Framed in the store-doorway was the unmistakable figure of Spell, looking inwards towards Clarke. The low sun pouring through the window into the smoky store revealed Spell's wiry frame in menacing silhouette.

Joe had seen more than enough of the man. He ducked out through the wash-house and into the exterior bicycle shed where he found Johnny Marsay astride his bicycle.

"Thank God for a friend," he gasped in Marsay's direction.

"I can't wait Joe, I'm in a rush. But I'll tell yuh, in there, there's that York driver, Spell, he's waiting for yuh, grumbling to Clarkey. A bit of queer beggar if yuh ask me. He's given Clarkey a note about your attitude."

"I could tell you that, mate," Joe replied as Johnny Marsay peddled off.

Joe set off running down Sander Road in the direction of home. His thoughts fully consumed by the events of the day.

A feeling of relief, like removing a heavy lead overcoat flooded Joe's body when he heard his Mother's greeting. "Who's that?" she called.

His reply was the conventional Yorkshire response, "It's only me?"

"Who's me?" Mother shouted habitually. He sank into a chair, still panting and clothed in greasy overalls. He attempted to give convincing replies to his Mother when she asked, "What's been happening at work today? You look worried."

He slowly revealed his anxieties to his mother even though he thought she would not understand.

"But you didn't hit him!" she gasped, as the tale unfurled. "What is it he wants?"

"I swore at him. I'd have hit him if Arthur Coleford hadn't pulled me back. He's saying I went absent from my post, well, I did run away."

"Can't you report him?" his Mother asked then added the retort. "You should never have gone on the railways."

"Mam, the only thing I could do, was get away before I hit him. He's written a letter saying that I am not suitable to be a fireman. It's an official complaint in writing. He showed it to Bill Clarke."

"Will you let your Dad go down and see him?"

"No. Good grief, Mam, I'm nineteen."

"You're Dad's Secretary of Castlebrough Trades Council."

"I know, but I don't care if he's Winston Churchill or Joseph Stalin. He's not going to fight my battles for me."

The two rest days passed with Joe at home, reading, thinking and gardening. He avoided talking about work to anyone but despite his monk like silence on the topic, his thoughts continued in a state of nervous agitation.

When Joe returned to work news came quickly to his ears. A rumour had circulated around the shed..., 'That Wadey had been scrapping with that York driver and he's been reported.'

"That's not true," Joe gave his honest reply to the question posed in the messroom. "I just had words with him. It's nowt worth talking about."

He rattled the newspaper he was holding. "I was just reading about that crash at Ferryhill," he said in order to change the subject. "The one where a goods train broke in two at five in the morning."

"And the back half ran into the front half," Alf South added. "Then the London express ran into the pile of wagons. That was 7th January. I remembered the date, it was on my birthday."

"There were three rail smashes in six days. The Home Secretary was one of the passengers. There's been about twenty deaths in total."

"Arthur told me you'd had a row with Spell," piped Alf.

Joe retorted irritably to Alf's renewed reference to Spell. "You said Arthur told you. Well he had no business to. I'm the one on the carpet with Franker. I don't want people talking about me."

"Hey, don't get shirty!" Arthur said firmly. "I pulled you off of him."

"Sorry, Art," apologised Joe. "Your right, you did."

"You've been on the carpet before, you'll only get a Caution or a Form One. They're just bits o' paper, they are," Art Coleford assured. "Nowt to worry about."

But Joe was worried, he had been reported as 'missing from his post' and of threatening to attack his driver, of being late for work, of swearing and of being a careless fireman. They were serious charges.

Arthur grimaced and said, "Looks unlikely to be a hanging job?" Joe squeezed his lips together but the others had a laugh at his expense.

"If it is," Hibbo shouted, "there's a good long tarry rope in the Fitters' Shop. Yuh'll get a dead load drop with that."

"I'm not having that round me neck. It'll make my collar dirty."

"No, no," chuckled Hibbo. "The rope's for Spell, not you Joe. You want all the limelight, let Spell do the swinging."

Days passed and driver Spell had not appeared at the shed. It was rumoured that he had gone back to York. Some said that he was ill at home. Joe tried to avoid asking about him, particularly as his name didn't appear on the daily roster. Joe's expected disciplinary action didn't materialise either, he talked about it though, continuing to express his anxiety. "I'm haunted by the waiting. I can't get him out of my mind."

"You know what the problem is," Alf declared. "You're under a Spell."

3
Red Light Spells Danger

"Hell of a morning," shouted Joe from behind his scarf, cap and high collared coat. He had just joined his driver for the day as they were both struggling towards the shed for a six a.m. shift on the station pilot. The biting wind and driving snow made conversation difficult. A muffled grunt was Harry's only response until they both entered the relative calm and smoky warmth of the loco shed.

"Glad I'm only on shunting today, I've had enough bad winters in recent years to last me a lifetime," sixty year-old Harry Tate declared. Bill Frobisher, night-shift running foreman and the messroom's only occupant, was leaning on the driver's roster desk as close to the raging fire as he could stand whilst writing. He exchanged greetings with Harry and Joe.

"Has the mail got through yet Bill?"

"No, it hasn't left York. This little lot's come down very heavily at York," continued Frobisher. "All the points are iced up."

"Who's takin' the seven-ten to Leeds if the Mail doesn't get through?" Harry asked, then asked the obvious next question. "Or is the seven-ten going to be cancelled?"

"Looks like you'll have to take it," replied Frobisher calmly.

"What," snapped Harry. "There must be somebody else."

"Your the only mainline man available, all the others on duty now are all local link men."

Harry chose not to argue, he knew he'd have to go. York control insisted that the seven-ten Leeds train would get through. The ploughs at York would soon have the through mainlines clear.

"It's alright for that flamer," Harry grumbled as he and Joe backed the loco out of the shed and towards Castlebrough Station. "He's sat in that shed, warm and bloody cosy. He doesn't have to go out in this damned weather." Fortunately, their one hundred and twenty ton B1 locomotive was in excellent condition for the task of working the ten coach-express.

"You lit the headlamps didn't you?" the driver asked of Joe.

"Yeh, and I've put the electric ones on too," Joe answered but secretly wondered whether he'd acted correctly by displaying two separate lights on the same lamp position. To Joe, the darkness and the falling snow justified having clear headlamp code lights on the front of the train. 'So why not show two lamps on each relevant position,' he reasoned.

When he'd started as a young fireman he'd at first thought that the lamp positions were to show others that a train was approaching. Then he learnt that the positions of the lamps on the front of the locomotive actually displayed to other trains and signalmen the type of train which was approaching. He worried about what others might make of four lights showing instead of two.

He asked Harry as they pulled away from the Castlebrough shed but Harry's answer merely displayed his hostility to 'modern gimmicky things'.

"I've been on the steamers so long," he said. "I just don't trust these modern electric gimmicks stuck on steam engines." He wrenched open the regulator and noisily set their engine on course to the passenger station. "Who the 'ell wants electric lights, self-cleaning smoke boxes, rocker bars, hopper ash pans?"

"I do," Joe remarked with emphasis as they clattered up to the waiting seven-ten in platform three.

"Why, they'll be putting showers and water-closets on engines next. Yuh young 'uns have never roughed it, that's why." Harry braked his loco so carefully that it gently squeezed the buffers up on the first coach as it came to rest. "Best go and hang on we're late," Harry's remarks were threaded with an strand of impatience. He wasn't pleased at the prospect of facing the main line in the storm so unexpectedly. His mood showed no sign of improvement when he heard the station inspector shout from alongside the cab door.

"Come on driver. You're late."

"To Hell with it," Harry replied as he created vacuum in the train brakepipe. Such remarks were really out of character for Harry who was usually placid and pleasant.

"The board's off, Harry and the guard's flagging us off." Harry could see the signals but he didn't object to his fireman Joe also repeating the fact. They worked as a team. That's how Joe saw his role and this mate had the same attitude. The engine whistle answered the train guard's whistle and the steam regulator put superheated energy behind the pistons.

"Just a mo'," Joe shouted as the train moved into life, "The lamps." Harry didn't hear the remark, engine noises dominated his hearing. Joe left by the cab door and climbed and clambered around the exterior footplate of the moving locomotive and alongside the boiler as the train built up forward motion. He reached the front end of the loco, stooped down from where he clung below the smoke box and switched off each of the two electric lamps. The wind and snow howled around him and he was suddenly struck with the realisation of how exposed to danger he was on the front footplate and beneath the smokebox of the rolling locomotive. A fall might place him under the engine wheels. As if to warn him the sponge cloth he held fell from his grasp below the locomotive and out of sight.

Common sense aroused him to his vulnerability and he quickly retreated back to the engine cab and Harry Tate's angry glare as the train's speed increased.

"Bloody daft thing to do!" Harry was furious. "You'll get yourself killed. Stupid." Joe received the admonishment without response.

The lamps were still as they had been, he'd been unable to see the aspect of the lamps. He explained his worry to Harry who closed a nearby electric switch after some consideration, "I think that might do the trick," he said.

"Good engines," commented Joe choosing to ignore old Harry's censure of his risky activities. "Just one problem with this class, the B1, it's a bad rider at speed. Like being on a bucking bronco when you're doing sixty," he shouted to Harry. His conversation existed for no other reason than to cover his embarrassment. Harry didn't reply.

Joe straightened from his firing task as they passed over the road crossing at Sander Station and the loco pitched sharply as it hit a drift of snow. "It nearly threw me off my feet. We're only going through Sander an' all." Harry was either ignoring Joe's remarks, or couldn't hear them above the noise of the train.

The harsh weather and snowfalls had made all travel difficult this winter. The snow ploughs had worked intermittently since the end of 1945. Joe recalled how he and Jim Woodley had hauled a buried passenger train out of snow drifts at Hawsker only months previous. The present unexpectedly severe conditions and weather forecasts indicated a worsening in the North. 'Was 1946 going to be as bad?' he thought.

The drag from snow that had settled on the rails slowed the train. The regulator was wide open and Joe laboured until the fire and steam pressure were at optimum levels. He turned to observe the line and the signals. Vision through the cab's spectacle windows was impossible, they were caked with snow.

Large soft snowflakes driven before the wind compressed on impact with the locomotive to leave a layer of snow on the well-lagged cylindrical boiler. The accumulating thickness hung there for a few seconds amid the air stream until gravity and the heat of the boiler forced the coating of snow to fall away.

"I've never seen snow settle on the boiler like that before," expressed the driver with surprise. Joe agreed, he'd never seen snow fall so rapidly, thick and virgin white, and deposit itself so quickly. He thrust his head out of his side window into the driving snow to view the line for Ganton's distant signal but withdrew it quickly. The snow adhered mask-like to his face and cap with three small holes where his eyes and mouth should have been.

Harry Tate laughed loudly at the vision as Joe brushed away his white blanket. He looked forwards into the snow, taking care not to subject himself to the same humiliation for longer than the briefest moment and caught sight of the distant signal at Ganton. It remained horizontal in the caution position until just before they passed it.

"Keep your eyes skinned for the cabin Joe. I'll watch for the home board." The loco rolled in the high wind, they were moving at about forty-five miles per hour. Harry closed the steam regulator and sounded the engine whistle but its scream seemed lost in the storm. "There may be a fog-man or a platelayer out at the level crossing, someone might be crossing by the side gate, yuh can't be too careful."

"The board's on," shouted Harry. The vacuum brake handle was immediately plunged into 'on' position for a rapid emergency stop. "Red light from the signalman, an' a flag."

"It's not the gates! they're open," shouted Joe. The advance semaphore signal beyond was also within their vision and in the danger position.

"To the cabin, Joe, rule fifty-five. Take a red flag and this hand lamp. The other line, watch it! there might be train coming." Small though he was, Harry Tate was the dominant person on the footplate. Calm in a crisis, dogged in defence, he soon relaxed after trouble. "Keep your eyes open."

Joe left the cab, protected only by his jacket and cap. 'Haven't time for an overcoat,' he decided. The snow and ballast and other unseen obstructions underfoot reduced progress to a mere struggling stumble. Everything seemed to be swallowed in the wind, muffled by the snow, or suffocated by the freezing temperature.

"You've got a red headlight on the front," the signalman shouted from the cabin steps to Joe as he closed on the cabin stairway. "What's matter?"

"Nowt!" Joe froze in his tracks. He was speechless, what could he say?

The signalman descended the wooden flight of stairs and shouted, "Sander West phoned. Thought he'd seen a red light. I'd given yuh the all clear. Had to throw all the boards back at yuh for safety."

"Do you want the train-book signing, rule fifty-five?" Joe wasn't frozen now, he was scheming. How could he avoid responsibility? Who else but him must be responsible?

"Get yourselves off as soon as possible?"

"But you'll have to report it. Won't You?" Joe asked nervously.

"Is that what you and your mate want?"

"No. Truth is, it's my fault. If you can say nothing, I certainly will?"

"You've stopped for steam right. I'll enter up in the occurrence book that yuh stopped 'cos o' snow an' steam. Now best go on an' see if yuh can get away again in this snow."

"Thanks mate," said the grateful Joe, feeling responsible for the wrong lamp code. He couldn't understand how it had happened. He made his way back to the train, corrected the red light, and observed that the coach doors were secured as far as visibility permitted. Driver Tate pipped his whistle and the train guard gave a signal for the train to depart. The loco heaved them into motion as soon as Joe climbed back on the footplate.

"What was that about?" the driver asked of Joe as the exhaust beat dominated the engine sounds and forward motion commenced.

"Don't really know," he lied, then changed his mind, the scheming that had gone on so desperately in Joe's head to avoid the blame was discarded, he told the truth about the red light at the front and how he had corrected it.

"That was a lesson for me Harry," Joe admitted after a long silence between them while they fought through the snow to Malton, "I'll never do that again. I'll always see that the lamps are in good order and showing the proper code. What a fright it was for me."

"It's what I told yuh. A lesson from the school of life, of life's experience," Joe nodded agreement as Harry explained. "You'll learn far more in working than you ever did at school." Joe wasn't so sure, why were schools and universities necessary if you were better schooled by experience at work?

Many passengers departed the train at York, those who remained were mostly for Leeds. Other passengers had longer journeys to complete. The slow drag from signal to signal or from fogman to fogman continued through the snow.

"Let's hope we get a run at Church Fenton Bank," said Harry as they toiled through Barton and Ulleskelf. Their wish was foiled. They were halted and then proceeded slowly up the rising gradient to Micklefield Junction. A little way beyond their advance signal a snow bound goods train blocked their path.

For the second time in the day Joe struggled forward on foot to the signal cabin at Micklefield to record rule fifty-five in the train book but first he went to see the crew of the goods train blocking the line.

"We've been here since four this morning." answered the fireman of the snow-trapped goods to Joe's query.

"There's one-line working all the way to Crossgates, isn't there?" Joe asked.

"Yes there is, I think," replied the fireman, who was about Joe's age, certainly no older. He displayed an uneasy disquiet and restlessness which was very obvious to Joe.

"You look as though you don't want to be here at all."

"I do want to get home. Last night, I clocked on at half past midnight to bring this goods down from Thirsk and I'm still here. My wife was rushed into hospital with stomach pains before I left for work. I can't get to phone the hospital. Where you from?" asked the Thirsk fireman.

"Castlebrough."

"Yuh might be home before me. Can yuh do us a favour? Get to a telephone box and ring the Cottage Hospital, Thirsk. Here's the number. Just leave a message for Elsie Johnson. Tell her I'm..., that is, me, Pete...., tell her I'm okay and will be home soon." Joe readily agreed. "Golly I don't know whether I'm coming or going."

"Whenever I get home. Yes, I will," Joe replied. "I'd best now get on before some thing happens and they give us a road." At that moment his mind took him back to his first mainline blockage, at Heslerton, when he'd backed the horses for Ankler and how he'd got a message through on the signalman's lines, 'Whistle Stop and Thistle Top,' the memory made him smile. 'Could he get a message through this time,' he thought.

"I might be able to do better than that," voiced Joe. "I've got to go to the cabin and record rule fifty-five, might be able to use their phone." Joe set off through the snow climbing the rising gradient as he went.

Time was short, he acted quickly. Up the wooden stairway and into the box he went. "Rule fifty-five. Oh. Can I use your line for an emergency call?" The line and the halted trains were on rule fifty-five train protection.

"Tell me your problem?"

Joe described the Thirsk fireman's concern. "Can you get a message to the Sister at the Cottage Hospital Thirsk.?"

"I'll ring our local Bobby, he's always very helpful," came the signalman's reply. He used his phone quickly and repeated the fireman's compassionate appeal to the answering policeman's wife.

"He'll call us back in a minute."

The return telephone call to the cabin occurred quickly. The signalman nodded and pointed, giving Joe the signal to take the mouthpeice.

"Yes, it is." He repeated each bit of the conversation for the benefit of the signalman. "She's fine, appendicitis, resting now."

After receiving the good news and passing on his own message Joe thanked the signalman and ran back to the Thirsk goods engine.

"Good news," he shouted as he approached, burning with pride at his initiative. He scrambled back on board the J class loco. "She's fine," Joe shouted and relayed the rest of the news. Joe's engine whistle sounded.

"I'll look you up Wade when I go to Castlebrough thanks mate, that was great of you."

Joe jumped from the cab of the Thirsk engine to the snowy ground, shouted his farewell, then, taking care to dodge an approaching express passenger train travelling to York under wrong line working rules, joined his own waiting express and driver. His own train was next to run back over the trailing crossover shunt onto the wrong line and travel to Crossgates and Leeds.

The passengers left the train after the six-hour journey, some to stay in offices or hotels overnight, or until normal services resumed. As soon as Harry and Joe received their orders they detached from the train and ran forward to a stop signal at the platform end where a train inspector was waiting.

"It's back home on the cushions mate," shouted the inspector to Harry Tate, "Your engine's needed urgently for a Harrogate and Thirsk run."

"We'll need a travel pass, do you want the engine leaving here or down by the canal roads as usual."

"Here's fine, the relief crew are here."

Joe and Harry obtained their travel documents and climbed aboard the stationary Castlebrough stock finding seats without difficulty. The bad weather had abated and a weak winter sun cheered travellers' hearts. Joe fell into a reflective state of mind and soon found his eyelids heavy after the day's toil.

A rat-a-tat on the glass panel of the compartment door caught Joe's attention. The door slid aside and the station inspector's head and shoulders appeared through the opening. "It looks like there's been a change of plan," he said. "Will you go and speak to control on the phone?"

"Summat's afoot," grumbled Harry as he pulled himself from the comfort of the carriage seat. "We'd best go and see what's happening." He dropped onto the platform and ambled across to the wall mounted box containing the telephone.

"Harry," said the voice over the line. "When I knew it was you coming in on the Castlebrough passenger, I said, just the lad to do this job."

"Skip the flannel," replied Harry. "I know whose behind that voice? What yuh wanting?"

"Someone to take that Gresley and train to Doncaster and onto Peterborough. Do you know the road to Peterborough? We're stuck for a set of men, the driver has just been taken to hospital. Sounds like he's maybe had slight seizure."

"Course I know the road to Peterborough. Just signed up for the route three weeks ago before I moved to Castlebrough."

"It's a long way from your working base," the station inspector cautioned Harry. "Yuh'll not get back home tonight, likely as not. What about your fireman?"

"Okay, don't worry about him. He'll do what I do."

"We're going, to Peterborough lad! with Sir Nigel Gresley?"

"Is he coming with us on the footplate?" asked Joe displaying complete innocence.

"He is the footplate, that's the 'Sir Nigel Gresley', the Loco over there on platform seven. We're being asked to take it through the snow with twelve bogies on to Peterborough."

The truth dawned on Joe. The pacific loco was like the 'Mallard', the holder of the world speed record for a steam locomotive. "Am I interested?" he said to Harry. "Course I am, It's not likely ever to get to Castlebrough."

"Get over there son. Let's be off before they change their minds."

His mind was in an excited spin. The locomotive was given it's name in honour of the famous locomotive designer, Sir Nigel Gresley. He piled into the cab in front of his mate eager to be well prepared.

"What yuh in a rush for," said Harry as he climbed aboard. "Yuh can't go without me."

Joe picked up the shovel and looked into the huge firebox. "Wow!" he exclaimed.

They placed their personal belongings in the iron locker on the forepart of the tender. Harry had his own oil can, as was the practice of most drivers. Even though locomotives were supposed to be tooled and ready for work, in reality many of the tools were battered or old and not good enough for the job. Thus many enginemen carried their own tools, Harry Tate always did. He instructed Joe to put it in the tool locker. Unbelievably, as he followed the instructions, the oil can lid burst open and oil splurted out all over the inside of the locker. Joe was horrified, but Harry hadn't noticed the mistake. Joe carefully closed the locker resolving to tell Harry later.

"Right we're off." Harry opened the regulator and the magnificent locomotive glided into forward motion. Joe couldn't wait to try the shovel but his eagerness was censored by Harry for firing too early and making black smoke in the station. Joe looked out and saw a huge mass of billowing black smoke above his head.

'Crikey, did I do that,' he thought to himself. The smoke settled like a dense black fog around the train.

"I can't see a thing, Joe," exclaimed Harry. "It's as black as pitch. I'm stopping." Harry applied the brake. "Go to the box Joe, rule fifty-five."

Before Joe could answer he found himself at the bottom of the signal box steps. He was up to his thighs in snow. "Joe Wade," a voice boomed.

At the top of the steps stood driver Spell and an important looking manager in suit and tie. Spell held aloft a red guard's lamp. Joe glanced up at the front of the A4 pacific, it had red lamps attached to all the lamp brackets. "Come on Joe," the voice boomed.

Spell stared angrily down from his lofty position whilst whispering to the manager. "Come on Joe." Joe tried to run but he couldn't move, his legs were held fast in the snow.

"Joe, come on, we're back at Castlebrough." Harry Tate was shaking Joe's knee. "Wakey wakey." Joe sat forward with a sudden start and opened his eyes to see Harry's smiling face beaming down at him. "You've been hard asleep since we left Leeds kid, we're home."

"Was I.... Crikey..., all ready," Joe gathered his thoughts as full consciousness returned him to reality. "I was just dreaming. About riding in the cab of an A4 pacific."

"Some dream, Joe," Harry said. "Reckon it'll be donkey's years before yuh do that!"

4
Whitby Willy

Mike Spell had not been seen for several weeks. In fact no-one talked or thought about him, except for Joe, who was still anxious and troubled by the charges that had been made against him. He couldn't enquire of the shedmaster, because he only knew of the written complaint through hearsay, as his shed-mates had told him. He might even be the victim of a hoax.

Tuesday morning saw him early at the shed preparing class A8 loco-motive number 9885 for the morning passenger train to Whitby. His mate Arthur Wilko was singing a popular tune from somewhere beneath the engine. Joe appreciated the happy atmosphere created by the plump and jovial Arthur Wilko. It was enough to allow the Spell problem to be soft-ened and tucked away into the back of his mind. With the loco prepared they ran smokebox first up to the station and coupled onto the waiting carriages at platform one.

"Is this the Whitby train?" asked frail, seemingly nervous lady about to board their train. Her red coat made her more prominent on the platform in the fast disappearing darkness. Her primrose woollen scarf and beige felt hat was indicative of a lively spirit, but she looked ill and rather sullen. She commented on the very changeable weather, "The snow, rain, and then the sunshine, all taking turns. But it is going to be lovely today." Her voice was unsteady.

"She does looks a bit ill, doesn't she Joe? "Stooping shoulders and a blank, sullen face. Maybe she's just old."

"Maybe," Joe agreed. "She's trembling too. She looks about ready to cry. I'll go and see her into the first compartment. Help her with her case." Joe reported on his return, "She says she's alright, only going to Whitby."

The journey up the bending and twisting, rising and falling rail track on the coast road to Whitby was always a delight to Joe, no matter what the season. Arthur's jokes and anecdotes made for an especially pleasant trip. Certainly in stark contrast to his journey with Spell who kept invad-ing his inner thoughts. He'd got into the habit of saying, 'I must cast this spell out of my mind.'

The spring-like weather helped Joe into a confident mood. The beat of the exhaust blast, the clickety-clack of the five-coach train, the hard climb to Ravenscar, the sudden exit from the tunnel to view the wide sweep of

Robin Hood's Bay and the North Sea, all helped dampen his anxiety. "It's a great line this one, don't you think Arthur?"

"Aye," Arthur nodded. "It'll be a great loss if it's ever shut down."

"You think that'll ever happen?"

"Who knows. If the line's aren't used much they get shut. I've heard of lines shuttin' because they can't compete wi' new road lorries an' buses."

"Nationalisation should sort it out, keep the railways going alongside the roads and canals. An integrated transport system that's what we'll have."

"I doubt it Joe," Arthur paused and sounded the whistle in response to a lineside notice. "I reckon they'll still be talking about that at the end of the century." Arthur chuckled, "We'll tell Jimmy Simpson that, eh. That'll get him going."

Whitby Station was almost deserted when the Castlebrough train pulled in. All the passengers departed quickly leaving only the red-coated lady trailing slowly down the platform.

They reversed their Loco out of the platform under the guidance of a shunter, turned, watered and checked their locomotive, then re-coupled to the train to await their departure at eleven am. They noticed the red-coated lady had occupied a station seat and was still there, motionless.

"Go and see if she's alright." Arthur instructed Joe.

"Yes I will, I was thinking of going for a short walk anyway." He removed his pocket watch and checked the time. "Shan't be long."

There was nothing particularly unusual about the red-coated lady, though she did look ill. "Are you alright," Joe enquired.

"Yes, I'm okay, just tired. I was so stiff, I just couldn't walk, so I waited and rested a while. I'm going home in a few minutes."

Joe wasn't so sure, she trembled when she spoke. "Mind if I join you." he asked.

A gentle smile flickered in her eyes even though her face was still set and worried looking. "Oh, its a long time since a young man wanted to join me," she said.

Slowly she revealed her recent misfortune and it's effect on her health. "I don't usually make a fuss. I'm sorry to be taking your time."

"You aren't. I say, if you haven't got time for people, you haven't got time for anything."

"No no! I won't bother you. I'm just a silly woman, a bit sick that's all. You won't want to know about me."

"I do," said Joe, "I like meeting people. Everybody has an interesting story to tell."

"Well," she relaxed a little. "I could tell you about railway engines in India and how I used to ride on them. I was born in India. I could tell you about the illness, the disease, I've just been diagnosed with, but I don't want to waste your time. Really, I'm ready to go home, I can feel the life coming back into my legs."

"Here let me take your bag."

"Alright, young man, if you must, but you're fussing. I like to be independent."

Joe took her bag and noticed that she was very unsteady. He grasped her arm and they walked slowly through the station arch into the town.

"How are you going to get home?" asked Joe.

"I'll walk its not far."

"Don't you want help? Or a taxi, you're trembling."

"No, I don't want a taxi. I'll walk. I need the exercise." After a short silence as they walked slowly. She resumed speaking. "I've just been in hospital."

"Oh!" responded Joe. "You've been in hospital. What's your name?" Joe asked.

"Everybody calls me Paddle, Peggy Paddle. Pauline Addleson is my real name but I'm Peggy Paddle to all my friends and I shake because of my illness."

"Tell me about your illness, I'll understand. My best friend is disabled, in a wheelchair."

"I've got a disease called Parkinson's. It makes you shake."

They walked very slowly. Joe stopped talking while they were walking.

"I'll go by myself now, I'm just up this hill. I can go up it slowly."

Joe was conscious about the time and his impending train departure, but he also felt a sense of responsibility for his infirm passenger. He'd come this far and he felt he had a job to finish. They stopped at a neat little terraced house on a road with a gentle gradient. He fumbled in his pocket for his watch, it wasn't there. 'Hell,' he thought, 'I've left it on the engine locker top, I'll Bet.'

Entry was bungled somewhat, Peggy Paddle had fingers that could maintain only a tentative grasp on small things, she fumbled in her purse, couldn't easily insert the key.

"It's not me, it's this fellow Parkinson on my back." She said, "Have you time for a cup of tea, a real Yorkshire welcome."

"I'll have to go to my train, perhaps some other time." They bade farewell and Joe set off back, breaking into a run. He now desperately needed to know the time. He took a wrong turning, he hadn't paid attention.

Eventually the station was in his sights and he ran in through the arch and onto the platforms. The station was empty, completely devoid of any rolling stock. His train was missing. "Oh hell!" he cursed under his breath. The station inspector was attracted by Joe's appearance.

"Hey son, are you the Castlebrough train fireman?"

"Yes, where is it?"

"Its gone." Was the blunt reply to Joe's question. "Couldn't wait any longer."

Joe looked at the station clock. "Six minutes late, I'm six minutes late."

"You'll be for the high jump, a big high jump, with a bloody hard landing." The station inspector's reply carried a little hint of glee in his voice, almost as if he took great pleasure at Joe's misfortune.

"Where'll he be now?"

"Oh," said the inspector slowly withdrawing his watch from his pocket and lightly tapping its glass face. "It'll be leaving West Cliff Station now, with a Whitby fireman aboard." He paused to take a sharp intake of breath through his nostrils. "Paid to do your job, young man. This'll mean big trouble for you."

"Can't you cover it up?" pleaded Joe. "I could pay the fireman, if you can fix it?"

The inspector couldn't believe his ears, this was corruption to him. Something that he could elaborate about at great length in his report. "That sounds very much like bribery to me." he said smugly.

"You are the station inspector, aren't you?" asked Joe.

"Ah. You've noticed me then. Where have you been?"

"I took a lady called Peggy Paddle home she was feeling sick."

The story was getting better. The inspector felt like the spider who'd just had a big juicy fly walk casually into his parlour. His eyes widened. "Peggy Paddlehome. Indeed!" His attitude suddenly became more aggressive. "Who the hell are you kidding young man?" He paused and glowered at Joe. "Mr Franker'll drop on you like two wagon loads o' coal when he 'ears of this escapade."

There was no room in Joe's head for a response of even the meanest kind. He turned, and, for the second time in the year that had just commenced, he ran from his duty, through the main exit and on to the station forecourt.

A vague idea about following his train circulated in his mind but external physical matters decided the course he was destined to take. He collided with an unseen vehicle and found himself sprawled across the forecourt cobbles.

The youthful afternoon-shift porter arriving for work on his battered Harley-Davidson motor cycle had run into Joe.

"Sorry," the motor cyclist said. His concern was clearly genuine even though Joe had given the impression that he was bent on committing suicide. The youth, with goggles up on his brow and his uniform railway cap worn in reverse, propped his motor cycle on its pedal stand and helped Joe to his feet. "Are you alright? What you in such a rush for?"

"I, I..., I should be on the train, the eleven o'clock one. But it'll be going over the Esk Viaduct any minute." Joe was nearly defeated. It was very, very important for him to be on his train.

"It's too late now. You've had it. You've missed it." the gravel voice of the pursuing station inspector, now closely behind, reminded Joe of the extent of his plight. "The high jump. That's all there is for you," he repeated with enthusiasm and cruel delight.

The porter detected the glee in the inspector's disposition. The inspector was of course his boss and he knew what a bully he could be. He immediately came to Joe's aid. "It's not too late, Let Lawrence of Arabia come to your rescue." The motor-cyclist stabbed his thumb several times at his chest.

"What Lawrence of Arabia?" questioned Joe as his mind grappled with the mental image of the legendary 'Lawrence' and how that was related to his own plight.

"Get on me bike. I'll take yuh. We'll catch the train at Hawsker. I'm not due on 'till twelve thirty."

"Go on then give it a try."

The bike was kicked off, roaring and spluttering, ready to go in a second.

"Who are you anyway?" enquired Joe, "Not Lawrence, eh?"

"Billy Whitely, Parcel Porter. Whitby Willy some call me." Billy's hands grasped Joe's railway cap and turned it back to front. "That'll stop it blowing away in the wind," said Willy. "Now, get yuh backside on t' back seat and we'll get off."

Joe did and almost fell off the back-end of the bike as it rocketed away down the quay side. They shot over the bridge that spanned the Esk and up the lanes and streets on the southern bank. He nursed a vision of himself falling off the back and being left unconscious in the road with his cap on back-to-front only to be found by a Whitby yokel saying. 'Ah. Ee wa nearly dead till I found 'im and turned his 'ead the right way round.'

The bike reverberated and backfired regularly, riding the hills, hollows and bumps with an indescribable frenzy of oscillations. Joe's eyes opened briefly, the red bricked buildings of the small Hawsker Railway Station flew by. They'd missed the train. It could be seen just ahead journeying towards Robin Hood's Bay with a gentle billow of steam puffing skyward from the chimney. He closed his eyes again and hoped that he would not be sick down the neck of his good Samaritan as they rolled from one side and then the other. The hedgerows flashed by at frightening speed until, with a final twist, the bike drew to a sliding, sideways-skidding halt on the platform of Robin Hood's Bay station. Joe was thrown from the saddle and into a heap on the floor where he became dimly aware of Arthur Wilko's welcoming groan.

"You'll be the death of me Joseph Wade."

The roar of the bike with the Whitby fireman now travelling pillion-passenger, receded at speed into the distance. Joe's sickness, which he feigned and exaggerated to avoid Arthur's inquest, soon disappeared and left him searching for explanations, excuses, lies or anything. He sliced his shovel smartly into the bunker then into the firebox to the rhythm of the exhaust beat as they left Robin Hood's Bay.

"You'll be the death of me, Joseph Wade," driver Wilko kept repeating without acrimony as Joe fired continuously and Arthur strove to make up for lost time. There was no heated condemnation of Joe by Arthur, just concern mixed with his eternal sense of humour.

"I heard that the York driver Mike Spell had complained in writing about you to Franker." Arthur shouted just they entered Ravenscar Tunnel. "Don't worry worse things happen at sea."

"Yes, but I'm not at sea," Joe shouted back. 'The high jump! Could it be possible?' Joe's heated imagination saw it as very possible, indeed likely. 'The sack, being fired, dismissed, your employment is ended, you're signing on,' The thoughts bounced around in Joe's brain like ping-pong balls. He knew of footplate men who had been dismissed. It would be the ultimate humiliation. The thoughts burned in his mind as he worked. A dip in steam pressure forced him to pay more attention to the reality of immediate concerns. He corrected the condition of the fire bed with the long fire irons. He fired more scientifically, steadied himself and then slowly explained to Arthur how he had missed the train at Whitby. One confession led to another, each revealing the detail of the next. The Driver

Spell incident, the red light on the front of his express and now missing his train at Whitby.

The burning anxiety about his recent misadventures troubled him all the way to Castlebrough and the shed. He knew that inevitable discipline would follow. As he walked towards the messroom he decided not to talk about the motor cycle episode. He pledged himself to secrecy as Arthur Coleford and Alf South approached him by the notice case.

"Hi Joe, guess what?"

Joe couldn't hide his alarm. "What?"

"Mike Spell's in Franker's office. He asked for you," reported Alf.

"Not trouble is it Joe?" Arthur response carried sympathy, he knew how much Joe was worrying about his run-in with Spell.

Joe responded grimly, "I tried to hit Spell at Darlington. He's put a complaint in about me. I'll be on the carpet in front of Mister Franker."

"You've been there before," Alf assured Joe. "Yuh might just get a caution, or a Form One. They're only bits of paper."

"Anyhow, what's this about being left at Whitby. Is it true? Somebody said he'd overheard something on the telephone network."

"Bloody hell. How do tales like that get invented?" Joe commented no more, he remembered his earlier promise of silence. "I'm going to the pictures now to see some real fiction." He signed off without further words to his two mates and prepared to walk home but curiosity and anxiety drove him to change his mind. He turned from his homeward direction and headed towards the roundhouse locomotive shed which housed the shedmaster's office. His approach towards the tall double wooden doors that closed the single line entry revealed sounds of talking from within. He paused, as he was about to unsneck the small personnel door, he thought he could hear Franker's voice. He listened intently then heard a soft feminine voice. 'A woman speaking' he said to himself. He didn't want to be caught eavesdropping if the door suddenly opened, it sounded like they were just the other side.

The sneck on the door suddenly clicked. Joe turned and ran quickly towards the external corner of the shed so as to be out of sight. Franker emerged from the personnel exit doorway, followed by a woman and Mike Spell, the elusive York train driver.

"Well, Mr Franker..., thank you so much. We will do as you suggest, won't we Mike."

The dominant figure who had once paraded, ordered and bullied Joe displayed a different bearing to the drill sergeant figure Joe remembered.

Gone were the hard features, the loud rasping voice, and commanding posture. Now the man snivelled, gasped and wiped tears away from his eyes as the woman comforted him. He listened intently but still only heard brief snatches of conversation. "Back to York...., after the war...., couldn't settle...., those times were terrible...., weren't they Mike?"

Joe saw Franker's hand rest comfortingly on Spell's shoulder and felt moved by what he saw. The man who'd bullied him so relentlessly was now a broken man.

"Thanks Mister Franker," the woman uttered again and again. Joe watched them walk away towards the steps that led up to Sander Road. Franker gave a final wave, then turned and re-entered the shed, closing the personnel door firmly behind him.

As soon as he felt he had an all clear, Joe skipped up the steps and onto Sander road but halted abruptly at the gate. He watched as the woman ushered Spell into the passenger seat of a car, then she herself got into the driver's side, started the engine, and sped off out of town.

Two days later when Joe was rostered for engine cleaning, and he and others were spread around in the works of an A6 tank engine cleaning the Stephenson's Link valve gear. A summons through the wheels of the engine instructed loudly.

"Wade, pick that tiny brain up and take it to Franker's office."

"Can he take his body as well, sir?" added Willy Wagget.

"I'll ignore that Wagget," Bill Clarke shouted. "Franker's got a letter. What have you been doing again, Wade?"

The motions were a cramped place for four cleaners to be threaded amongst. "A thoroughly enjoyable experience to submit your best men to," Alf moaned as he wiped black paraffin out from his neck that had just dripped from Arhur Coleford's rag.

"Come on Wade. Get yuh backside up there. Or shall I tell Franker yuh want the sack?" Bill Clarke could be exceedingly uncompromising when he wanted to be.

Joe organised himself and knocked on the outside door of Franker's two-roomed office, entering only when he heard Franker's voice.

"Come in," Franker shouted. "Oh! It's you Wade. Yes, Wade, I needed to see you."

Joe noticed he said 'Wade', and not 'Joe' as was often usual. When Franker used surnames, it was a portent of worse to come. Joe stood quietly, cap on head, even in the boss's office.

"Now then, what was it son?" he flicked through some papers. "Of course." He didn't pause long enough for Joe to draw a breath. "You fool-hardily put yourself at considerable risk on the front of engine, a B1. You were on an express to Leeds, when it was snowing heavily. Do you remember?"

Joe's brief admission was followed with a curt, "I'm sorry."

"Well. Don't bloody well do it again. I don't like having to write reports about accidents. Consider yourself told off. Next time you might just lose your legs, or even your head to Madame Locomotive Guillotine."

A long pause followed as Franker scribbled on some paper.

"Is that all Sir?" Joe was so nervous that he unintentionally invited further condemnation upon himself.

"No, there was something else. Do you know what it is?" he stared at Joe, as if to intimidate an answer from him.

"Could it have something to do with a red headlamp?" Joe asked.

"What about a red headlamp?" Franker hadn't been informed about the stop at Ganton, so he asked Joe to explain then continued. "So, you were rewriting the headlamp code. Eh?" Franker sank back into his chair and drilled his pencil on the desk. "Well, write it out on paper next time. Learn it absolutely thoroughly and then tell me when it's permissible for a red light on the middle bracket."

Another long pause followed.

"You've no more surprises for me, have you?" added Franker.

"Do I get anything against me, a Form One or a caution?"

"An entry in the book. I'll show it as 'corrective instruction given', that should suffice."

"Thanks Mr Franker. Is that all then?"

"Are you sure you've told me everything, Joseph?" Franker produced two letters from his drawer. Joe was horrified. "A little bird tells me that you missed you're train at Whitby the other day." Franker paused, screwing his eyes up. "Had to hitch a lift on a motor bike. That true is it?"

"More or less, Mr Franker."

"More or less! Well I hope the bloody motor bike had L.N.E.R. painted on both sides, we can't have you riding on L.M.S. stuff whilst your in the pay by the London and North Eastern. Can we?"

"Er no sir, I suppose not."

Franker picked up one of the letters. Joe's stomach turned over.

"I've a letter here from a Miss Addleson of Whitby, she expresses her most sincere thanks for the young man who escorted her home. I presume that was you, wasn't it?"

"Yes sir."

Franker's attitude softened for a brief moment, "Very commendable," then he hardened again. "But being late back to the station delayed many other passengers and that cost the railway company unnecessary expense."

"I felt sorry for her, sir, she has an illness."

"Yes," Franker leaned forward and spoke emphatically. "But when they buy a railway ticket, we're only contracted to deliver them as far as the bloody railway station."

"Sorry Sir."

"I'll let this drop this time, but no more acting like a Knight in shining armour. Is that clear."

Joe nodded. "May I go now, Sir?"

Franker didn't answer but picked up the other letter and looked at it intently as if he was reading it word for word. After what seemed to Joe like an eternity, he let the letter fall back to his desk.

"Mike Spell, the York driver who was sent to work here," Franker paused as if waiting for an answer. "You accompanied him to Darlington didn't you?"

"Yes," Joe was now filled with terror. If Spell was reduced to tears in Franker's office what fate was about to befall Joe.

"The poor chap," Franker's voice mellowed. "He's been retired from service. He had a nervous breakdown and spent two weeks in a mental institution." For a moment Joe wondered whether he was the cause of this misfortune. Franker continued. "He was an officer in the army during the war, got awards for bravery, but he just couldn't cope with civvy street, he couldn't re-adjust."

"Oh, I didn't know."

"I just thought you might like to know what became of Spell." Franker picked up the letter again. Joe knew that Franker knew what had happened, he braced himself, but this time Franker smiled. "Now, back on duty, Mr Wade. Remember, I don't want to see you again on discipline."

Franker waited until Joe had left his office. He took one last look at the letter and gently tore it into several pieces letting them cascade into his waste basket. "Poor chap that Spell," he said to himself allowing a little sympathetic smile to flicker across his face.

1
Gone with the Wind

"South! "What the 'ell are yuh doing in there?"

Alf South, didn't pause for one second, "Cleaning the brick-arch down Sir," he replied loudly from within the firebox of A8 side-tank locomotive 9881. Alf always addressed Mr Franker as 'Sir', but then Alf was an unusual locomotive cleaner; he didn't swear, he didn't smoke, didn't even look at French postcards according to shed gossip.

"Who the hell told you to clean in there?" demanded Mr Franker kicking open the fire-hole door a couple of notches then bending to look into the firebox. He could see Alf's very dirty face, illuminated by a naked paraffin flame, looking out to meet his gaze.

"Didn't you. Sir? When you told us to clean every bit of 9881."

"I didn't tell yuh t' wipe its arse. Come out, for Lord's sake. Thank God we won the war before they got you in the army."

"Comin' Sir." He passed the lamp through the door and, before following the lamp, turned back into the firebox and whispered into the darkness, "Stay there, Joe, else you'll lose the job tomorrow."

Joe Wade's instinct was to call back, 'What job?' but the shed master's voice returned with the demand to Alf South that he bring the playing cards out with him because it was time to light her up.

Joe choked momentarily at the thought of shovels filled with blazing coals entering the firebox with him inside. Alf scrambled through the fire-hole door, his head and shoulders coming out first and blocking off all light to beleaguered Joe.

"I haven't got any cards, Sir."

"For God's sake stop calling me Sir, you aren't at school."

"Yes Sir. Sorry Sss...., We've cleaned the engine. The tubes have been swept and the boiler plate scraped. A great heap o' muck left on the brick-arch. The boiler-smith said it wanted removing."

"Have you removed it?" queried Franker. He didn't wait for an answer before asking, "Where's the others?"

"Finished, gone home, they've been on night shift. There's only me and Joe Wade on days, today."

Franker grunted acknowledgement and left the engine cab by the driver's side and walked off in the direction of the shed stores and Bill Clarke. "The A8 in number two road, 9881, send her on the film job tomorrow."

Franker ordered the chargeman. He handed over the papers. "Here's the working, its been changed again. They're all set for tomorrow now."

"Can't make their minds up eh?" asked Bill Clarke.

"The weather and the sun has got to be just right for the film crew." Franker replied.

Alf South was just approaching the store and caught most of Franker's remarks, especially the question, "Who have we got working the train?"

"It's West and Wade," answered Bill Clarke. "The two 'W's. The Worst in the World, that's what I call 'em. Troublemakers, both o' them."

"Not that bad surely?" asked Mr Franker.

"Kiddin' I am really. But I never let Wade forget he dropped his plugs at Ravenscar. And Tom, well he's always on at us about conditions. Argued about this job going to Wade 'cos he's the only one getting the twelve hour rest period."

"Was he right then?"

"Alus is," cracked Bill Clarke, now wishing he had never started on his joke about the two 'W's.

"I want that engine clean and shiny. Get some tallow on t' make the paintwork shine. Get her spruced up."

"Wade's about somewhere today," interjected Bill.

"Wade and West have new uniforms issued for this job. Get them to call at the top office before they go home." He placed an envelope on the desk. "Give this programme working to Tom West."

"Wade's about somewhere," Bill repeated. "On days, cleaning, he was cleaning 9881. With you Alf, wasn't he?"

"Where is Tom West?" the shed master asked and then realised, "Oh, course he's on the early coal pilot, I saw 'im pass the office. Get 'im and Wade in 'ere. I'll gi' 'em their instructions."

"Joe Wade's here, Bill," interrupted Alf as Joe walked into the store wiping his washed face on a clean sponge-cloth.

"You, Alfred, get over t' coal pilot. John Davis is firin', get 'im to tek over Tom West's driving and you, Alf, you do the firin' on the coal pilot."

Alf moved quickly to take up the unexpected promotion. But Bill Clarke demonstrated his knowledge of the shed floor protocol and intervened.

"Can't do that Mister Franker, you've got to use Mason to fire in Davis's place. Mason's the senior cleaner on the day shift, it's his job according to the agreements."

Alf South's jaw dropped displaying his disappointment. "That would have been my fourth firing shift since I started. How about it Mr Franker, I'm keen an' willing to do it."

"It's Mason's job, he's the senior cleaner in the shed today after Wade, 'till the one o'clock shift comes on."

"Wade can't go. I want 'im in the office. That's the whole idea."

"Well, Mr Franker, yuh'll have t' pay Wade and Mason firemen's pay today. Tom West an' the L.D.C will drop on us like a ton o' bricks if yuh don't."

"Who the 'ell is the shedmaster here?" Franker glared. "Me or the Local Departmental Committee? You sort it out. On your 'ead it lies."

Bill Clarke didn't offer anymore advice. He felt that he had done enough to harm his relationship with the shedmaster for one day. He knew that he was correct and he knew that the shedmaster would agree once he'd thought it through. Deciding who got the senior job was often an issue that provoked dispute amongst the men. A job carrying more pay might be rightly claimed by two men, and they might each have an equal claim; victory for one was disappointment for the other.

"What's the film about?" asked Tom West after he was relieved of his driving duty by Davis and given the news that he and Joe were going to help make a film. They'd joined Shedmaster Franker in his office to receive specific instructions.

"Driver West and Passed Cleaner Joe Wade," as Franker had addressed them, were to crew a train on the morrow using Class A8 side-tank engine 9881 and with good fortune they would feature in the finished film. Curiosity and excitement boiled in Joe's stomach, he would like to see himself in a film even if only briefly.

"Does the unions agree, especially the actors' unions?" asked Tom West, forever the A.S.L.E.F. branch secretary, and forever chairman of the Local Departmental Committee. Always vigilant to ensure that agreements were enforced; he was always well rewarded by the shed electorate by being voted into the office again. Tom's energetic movement and decisiveness, and his satisfaction at waging and winning battles with the shedmaster made him almost universally liked even though the frantic waving of his arms, 'like a bloody windmill', while talking very loudly at speed was always irritating to his fellow workmen.

"I'm not sure what film it's going t' be except it's not a railway training film. It says here," He tapped the papers he was holding in one hand. "It says that it's going t' be a feature film about a holiday camp, something like Butlin's Holiday Camp at Filey." Franker paused and fingered through the foolscap sheets of paper. "The train working doesn't show you at Filey, it says you'll be under the film director's instructions for your movements between Whitby West Cliff an' Kettleness."

"There's no holiday camp up there," Tom West stated the obvious, they all knew that part of North Yorkshire very well. Franker explained that the location of the first 'take' was at Sandsend about four miles north of Whitby West Cliff. It was just north-west of Whitby town and the high brick built thirteen-arch, viaduct spanning the River Esk. Tom was cautious about the film venture. He voiced his concerns. "The Transport Bill is just before parliament. I hope some big chief isn't planning a propaganda coup. There's a lot of opposition to the nationalisation of the railway companies by major shareholders and managers."

"I don't know why that should be," added Franker rising to Tom's bait. "There's no guaranteed profits and it isn't easy to sell railway shares." Franker, realising he was being drawn onto political grounds, decided to finish his contribution and change the subject. "The Government is going to buy them all at a fixed price anyway."

Joe pursued the other question, "What is a feature film? You mean a feature film like 'Gone with the Wind'."

"Tha's good at making wind," Tom West spluttered out, pouncing on the opportunity to have a joke at Joe's expense.

The shedmaster adopted the same spirit, "Yes, just like 'Gone with the Wind'. Though knowing you two characters, Charlie Chaplin and the Keystone Cops springs more t' mind."

"I'll be Clark Gable," chipped in Joe grinning widely at the suggestion.

"You'll be Chaplin," said Tom West. "More your type, especially the big flat feet."

"And the mouth." Franker added without much further merriment and turned their attention to the job in hand. "A set of five thirds and firsts non-corridor stock will be on number two platform. Go bunker-first from the shed then take the train empty to Filey for the passengers. 'Film extras', that's what they are calling them, will board the train. A good impression, that's what the General Manager wants for the Company. An' if they come on the footplate wi' a camera, just be sure to have it sparkling tidy and clean." He leant forward across his desk and peered towards the floor. "Polish your boots Wade, and, the pair o' yuh, come in a collars and ties and your new uniforms."

The evening shift of engine cleaners were attempting to strike a deal with Running Foreman Frobisher. "Up and home. That's what we've been promised, Bill." South and Wagget were urgently pressing their demand forward into Bill Frobisher's ears.

"Get on with the job. I'll tell you skiving beggars when you are finished." Bill Frobisher, was preparing his stance for a deal. He knew how best to get work out of engine cleaners whose principal interest was to be out on the locomotives gaining firing shifts. He'd been given his orders by York H.Q. and he was going to make his charges do more engine cleaning than they'd ever done before. Orders to him had been; 'Engine crew and engine turned out smartly and efficiently, expect a camera visit on the footplate and all locomotive ash and clinker to be wagonned.' Lean, hard-nosed Frobisher got the cleaning gang of eight together. "When I say it's finished, it's finished and not bloody well until I say so does anybody dare t' go home."

He ignored most of the back chat; he gave them their orders. Quite a number of them had served in the services during the recent war, they could be tough and undisciplined if they wanted to be that way, and they were older than Joe. "You guys know the score, play ball wi' me an' yuh can be 'ome or in the Railway Tavern by eight. Beggar me about an' you'll lose two hours pay for work not done and going early. Now yuh got that? Ain't yuh. If yuh want t' see if I can be tough now's yuh chance."

They co-operated with Frobisher's remarks echoing in their heads and got their elbow grease into action in double quick time.

The smoky stale atmosphere in the old bar at the Railway Tavern contrasted horribly with the clean air of the light August evening. Wagget and his fellow comedians were engrossed in the game of Solo for relatively high stakes, others discussed work, war or politics.

"Hey up." Wagget cried out. A smartly suited Joe Wade had appeared in the bar and caught Willy Wagget's eye. "Who's a right bobby-dazzler then. A star is born eh, bound for Broadway and Hollywood." The card game abruptly halted as the others turned to see what was tickling Wagget.

"Hey Wadey, when you make it," one of the card players called out. "Send me a worn out Hollywood actress." He crudely gesticulated with his cupped hands as if clutching a woman around the buttocks. "Sure, I could rejuv...., rejuv...., rejuvenate her."

"Yuh can't, it's obvious yuh can't do it. Yuh just an aw'd ram,"

"Fill us in on the film, job Joe?" Alf South asked as he was feeling slightly uneasy about the nature of the chatter.

"If you're going t' listen," insisted Joe. "I will, but I'm on me way down town tonight."

"Drinks all round, then we'll listen."

"If it's going t' be Adam's Wine, okay," he paused, they were listening. "We go t' Filey, t' pick up the passengers, the extras they call 'em, Oh, an' Flora Robson's one name I remember, and Jack Warner, then, bunker-first straight up t' Whitby West Cliff. When they're ready, and the section's clear for long enough, we take them all on t' Sandsend Station then on t' Kettleness where we run 'round the train. Then we come back to Sandsend Station where they film us arriving."

"What just arriving? New gear an' all that engine cleaning, all that fuss just for that," Alf seemed to be disappointed and with the seeming anti-climax, the others began to lose interest too. Attention drifted back to the card game.

Joe stayed awhile and had a quick half-pint. "Right you lot, I'll 'ave t' go, got t' be up early." He then emphasised the rest of his sentence. "T' be on the film set." Joe's parting remark drew a chorus of groans from his fellow workmates and drinkers.

"Get away wi' yuh. Clear off yuh daft begger."

The sunny August morning in 1946 when they arrived at Filey Town started disappointingly for Joe. There was no film set, no film stars, no director on a folding chair with a sunshade over his eyes and his mouth bellowing instructions into an amplifier. Just holidaymakers with suitcases, some prams and pushchairs and an invalid wheelchair that had to be lifted bodily into the guardsvan. It was just like an ordinary crowd of home-going campers, no cine camera on a tripod to be seen anywhere.

Joe feigned disappointment. "An' I polished me cap. What a waste. I combed mi' 'air too. Nearly changed me socks. Damn it chaps!"

"Keep yuh hair on if yuh can, as they say in America before they electrocute yuh in the chair," added Tom.

"But I wanted to be in that film," mocked Joe.

"Give over whinin'," Tom West stated and added. "Who wants t' be a shadow on a bit o' celluloid anyway?"

"I would o' seen 'em Tom, when we ran 'round the train." Joe had walked along the platform gazing into passenger compartments but there were no faces to be recognised.

"I did see Ginger Rogers in the third coach," Joe said mischievously.

"Oh yeh, an' I'm the Man in the Moon," Tom West declared sarcastically as he tugged the whistle cord to terminate the conversation with a shrill blast. The train set off bunker first on the journey back through Sander Junction and Castlebrough.

As they passed Castlebrough locomotive sheds, Wagget and the other's who had cleaned the engine were in the yard waving, shouting and hooting as if Fay Wray and Vivien Leigh were aboard the train.

Without stopping the train at Falsgrave signal cabin, they collected their single line electric token and entered the curved tunnel which passed beneath Castlebrough. Their journey then continued by single line coast road towards Whitby through Ravenscar and Robin Hood's Bay.

The journey pleased Joe and Tom as they noisily invaded the sparkling lively day. The heavy foliaged trees and bushes, thick and close to the curving, undulating track, muffled the roar at the chimney head and the morning sunshine danced on the trail of steam and smoke that they left in their wake.

They climbed the long 1 in 40 gradient to Ravenscar, exchanged the hooped tablet without stopping and entered the downhill Ravenscar tunnel with the steam valve closed. No exhaust beat sounded as they coasted downhill in the blackness of the short tunnel. Their speed gently increased and the wheels noisily squeaked on the check-railed bends that rolled between the wet tunnel walls. Then in a moment they emerged suddenly into the blaze of daylight, greenery, bright sky and scattered cloud to descend the falling gradient that would lead them on and down to Robin Hood's Bay. Gulls swooped in their part of heaven, their calls unheard in the steaming noisy locomotive cab. The broad sweep of Robin Hood's Bay extended as a green and blue carpet of nature to the distant horizon.

This most beautiful stretch of the old coast railway to Whitby would always fire Joe's imagination with romantic and poetic thoughts. Especially the northbound journey which was downhill. He rested on his fireman's seat and drew from his pocket his small notebook. The clatter and cacophony in the cab ebbed to the back of his mind. Tom West, calm and in control on his driver's seat, drifted into the background of Joe's visual consciousness. He pencilled his poetic thoughts in the little notebook and mused over them as his inner voice spoke the verse that struggled for birth;

Thoughts on a footplate journey
from Ravenscar to Robin Hood's Bay.
They have not lived, those who have not come this way
and
felt the balm of nature's calm, soothe life's affray.

Watched random blossoms, seeds, leaves and trees
dress the track with grasses, birds and bees
and
seen rabbit, stoat and sheep, some heeding, some asleep.

Together they conspire to cushion life's blast
return to balance bird song with beauty at last
and
create the day for peace and play, in all of nature's cast.

"Hope yuh keepin' yuh eyes open," Tom West yelled surprisingly in Joe's ear, "That was the platelayer's trolley standin' off the line. Yuh should've shouted. Yuh'd a seen 'em before me if yuh'd been looking out." His annoyance with Joe was real enough. The three men with the petrol-engined rail trolley were safely clear of the track while the train passed. "Keep yuh eyes open, stop dreaming, 'specially when there's a trolley on the line."

Joe nodded, mouthed "Sorry", pocketed his scribbling book and intently watched the Fyling Hall station platform pass by. He paid attention for the rest of the way through Robin Hood's Bay on towards Prospect Hill Junction and Whitby West Cliff.

"Here we are," Tom was almost speaking to himself as he responded to their arrival at Whitby West Cliff Station. Joe surrended the hooped tablet to the signalman as they entered the station. His interest in their 'feature film mission' was now reviving.

Passengers were leaving the compartments and standing around, imbibing the clear air and the warm August sunshine; nothing distinguished them from an ordinary train load of passengers. Tom and Joe's train was awaiting the arrival of the morning Middlesbrough service that would leave the line vacant for the next two hours. Only then could they, and the film crew, occupy the singe line as far as Kettleness.

"Driver! Hello!" The call reached Tom West's ears as he was drying his face on a sponge cloth after a hurried wash in the engine bucket. Joe was bent to the task of sweeping the cab floor with his handbrush so he had likewise been unprepared for the visitors pressing at the cab doorway. Tom looked over the door top, "Yeh, What d' yuh want?"

"It's Tom West, you troublesome ol' beggar. Just the lad I'd 'ave wanted on this job. Summat's bound to go wrong now."

"Now!" Tom bellowed. "Now! summat's already bloody gone wrong if you're on the job. We don't want a loco inspector with us so clear off." He tumbled, almost fell out of the cab and grabbed the bulbous figure, whose characteristics; reddening nose, bleary eyes and the girth of a small carthorse, betrayed him as a heavy drinking man. A timid looking, trilby-hatted companion of the loco inspector stepped hastily to one side to be clear of Tom's apparent coming assault. Tom's arm shot out and belted the inspector on the shoulder, then his other arm flew around him and the assault became an embrace. Tom hadn't seen the loco inspector since the big German air attack on York station in 1941.

"How the 'ell are yuh Charley, I sent a big bunch o' dandelions when I 'eard you'd got bombed," Tom uttered insensitively.

"Yuh didn't, there weren't no dandelions out in November."

"Yeh, but I waited 'til summer, there was some then, an' anyway, I was waiting to see if you was going to pop-off before I got 'em for yuh."

"Five years, no six, since I got hit." Charley responded thoughtfully with a measure of sadness in his face, after all several of his colleagues had perished on that fateful night.

Tom West read the sign and boiled up with fresh optimism, deliberately avoiding the memories he knew were in Charley's past. "What are we doing today Charley?" he bubbled on. "That's the burning question, an' there's my whippersnapper mate here." He pointed to Joe. "He wants to know if he gets actor's union rates on this job." Joe was pushed forward as an introduction.

"I'll tell you what we want, Mr West," broke in Charley Brown's trilby-hatted companion. "I'm the director for the Gainsborough film company, hope you don't mind me taking charge, so to speak. Just the train's movements, I'm meaning. Not taking charge of railway operating."

The line cleared to Kettleness whilst they talked. The questions came thick and fast. Tom pressed his unusual company, "Anythin' yuh want just ask. As long as it's in the rules, I'll do what yuh say," Tom continued, "and if it ain't in the rules we'll have to put it in." Then still looking at the director added, "We'll do anything for this old pal, Charley here. We're obliging fellows, me and Joe. He's me fireman." Tom West, now having asserted himself in front of his new companions, quickly heaved himself into the engine cab and said, "Come aboard, bring yuh cameras." Tom's associated wild gesticulations urging an immediate response offered no chance to decline. The inspector and the director climbed onto the footplate when the signal to go was given to leave for Sandsend.

"A lot of metal viaducts along this stretch of line. Unique scenery?". queried the director as he peered through the cab doorway.

"Yeh, there's four viaducts, on metal pillars, tubular, they are. Feel 'em shake as yuh go over. There's Sandsend Viaduct, up ahead an' that's Sandsend Station just past it.

"Are you another Alfred Hitchcock?" asked Joe, with an obvious grin indicating that the question was meant to be light-hearted.

"Sort off, I'm a director. I've worked with Hitchcock once."

"Shut up Joe." Tom had to be in, "Let the organ-grinder talk, not the monkey. I'll ask the questions. What is it you want to do? What are we to be doin' 'ere, go on matey, tell?"

"He will if you ever shut up, Tom." chipped in Charley.

They learnt of the film director's programme. They were to pull the train with it's passengers up to and through the first mile-long Sandsend tunnel and on through the shorter Kettleness Tunnel, then on to Kettleness

Station. On arrival they would have to run their engine around the train and then return with the train through the tunnels and back to Sandsend drawing steadily into the station so that the passengers, 'the holiday makers', could impatiently start leaving the moving train.

"Before we're off, I'll just shoot you two sweating away on the engine. Make it look real you chaps."

"Course it'll be real," pronounced Tom. "He's a real fireman, and I'm a real driver, I don't look like a gorilla, do I?"

Tom West brought the train to a steady halt at Sandsend Station. The small seaside village located on a particularly beautiful and rugged piece of North Yorkshire coast was served by just one platform. Joe took a moment to gaze up the line ahead. The track picked its way along a ledge cut into the spectacular rock face that rose almost vertically from the shoreline.

"It's a beautiful backdrop against which the approaching train can be filmed," commented the director. "It'll be the main study today, with the extras and some of the leading characters filmed as they leave the train."

Their visitors cheerfully left the footplate. "We're taking no chances," Tom West said to Joe. "We'll check that everything is in good working order. I know you say it were all done at the shed. That's what you were thinking," Tom emphasised. "Never mind, check it, summat might just 'ave broken down. Clean the sand valves, check that there's water in the tank, check everything; detonators, flags, oil. Yuh know what to do, if yuh don't, yuh shouldn't be 'ere."

"There is one thing I'm a bit bothered about," confided Joe, "There's a very bright part in the fire, I think we've lost a fire bar. Down on the left front set." Joe pointed into the firebox.

Tom peered in "Aye, you'll be losing fire into the ashpan, and cold air'll get through up by the firebox wall. Try spreading out the firebars, using the long straight dart. D' yuh understand what I mean?" Joe did know what he meant. With both ease and alarm he recalled silently when he and Alf South had been in the firebox and removed some firebars to allow them drop muck and clinker through into the firebox ashpan. The clear memory haunted him of how he deliberately left a firebar withdrawn when Franker was shouting into the firebox.

He knew, there was no doubt, he had removed it and failed to replace it. The memory would become more indelible with the passage of time, like the memory of throwing his firing shovel into the firebox on that night-time express. He vowed that he would never speak to anyone about this event, not even if he became a devout catholic and started attending confessions.

The locomotive inspector was not informed about the missing firebar.

"Maybe it won't cause us much trouble, might just make steam a bit more slowly, not bound to start a collapse of other bars," Tom whispered.

"I thought she wasn't steaming quite right when we pulled up the bank from Staintondale," Joe replied. "I know this loco, 9881, better than back o' mi' hand."

There was too little time to do anything to remedy the situation. The cameraman's assistant visited them with clear instruction "Take the train to Kettleness, we're staying here with the cameras on the stands. The director says you know what you'll be doin' at Kettleness. When you come back, out of the tunnel, make her smoke a bit, make her noisy and lively, blow your engine whistle, show your faces," he said. "Show your faces when you are running into Sandsend Station."

"Don't want 'im showin' 'is face," Tom said indicating at Joe, who beamed alongside full of anticipation. "The public watchin' the film'll think it's a cattle train when they see his head stuck out." Joe shook his fist under Tom's nose in a mock threat. "Yuh can shout moo as often as yuh like," Tom added defiantly. Joe responded more aggressively. "And yuh can stick yuh what's it ou' the cab and manure the plant beds as we pass."

Tom's closed the music hall session with a rude rasp and reached for the regulator. The engine barked into life and heaved the five coach train forward. They were on a gently rising gradient which would soon become steeper and continue to rise until they reached Kettleness.

Tom West had his attention riveted to other matters now; he tried the regulator in full open position in his haste to get early momentum; the driving wheels spun wildly causing sparks to stream from each of the driving wheels; Tom had been too keen to accelerate and demonstrate the engine's potential to the film-making party.

He closed the regulator, operated the sanding control handle and opened her up again the moment she found her feet. He nodded approvingly as the loco roared a powerful message to the film makers.

"Get her going Tom, let's show them what she can do. Make her go." Tom needed no further encouragement he was showing off like a school kid, savouring the instant kick, as 9881 burst forward with acceleration.

3
A Lifeless Run

A slight haze hung in the atmosphere above the rocky headland, not enough to create a rain shower, just a damp mist which might settle easily on the dusty rails and produce a thin layer of slippery lubricant. But the crew didn't feel any concern. Joe was feeling good at being in action again, on this, a memorable stretch of line for him. The gaping hole down the left side of the firebed didn't concern him greatly, he would use large pieces of coal to bridge the gap until they either burnt away or dropped through to the ashpan.

She was going now, she was striding away, up the gently rising gradient towards the distant tunnel mouth, higher up, but still not in view. To their left the shadowy high rock face dominated with its neatly cut stone faced retaining wall which passed by Joe almost within touching distance. Above and out of sight beyond trees and bushes were the old mine workings. To their right the North Sea stretched away from its rocky shore to meet the sky at a ship dotted horizon. In front, the stone portals of Sandsend tunnel, which would take them through one mile of rock, beckoned them forward. Joe fired carefully and scientifically, keeping his fire bright to avoid making too much smoke. He kept the firebed in text-book order with the one exception of the problem caused by the missing firebar. As the hole gaped he fed in lumps of coal to bridge it briefly.

The stone portals of the tunnel devoured them suddenly as their bunker-first engine plunged into the darkness. The wet rails within the tunnel caused the wheels to slip momentarily but were soon controlled by Tom.

"Yuh alright with that fire?" Driver West addressed Joe. "Yuh losing water level." Tom nodded at the gauge glass. Joe agreed. He fired selectively, the journey through the inside of the rock headland slowly and undramatically passed by. Blackness retreated before daylight as they emerged from the mile long tunnel. A short run along the cliff faced track bed was followed by the shorter Kettleness tunnel, then out into the brightness of the day again. At Kettleness station they ran their engine around the train and Joe took time to look beneath his locomotive at the ashpan.

He half expected to see fire falling through and filling the ash pan, but it was looking worse than he'd imagined. "Just my luck, an' on a special film run, we break down. I'll have to do summat."

"An' what's summat goin' t' be?" Tom sounded impatient.

"I'll try and empty the ashpan, but its going to be difficult without an inspection pit."

With the engine handbrake firmly screwed down Joe wriggled between the wheels and lay lengthways between the rails. He used the bent dart, the long pricker, the clinker shovel, anything that came to hand, even a platelayer's metal forked garden rake, to clear the burning fire from the ashpan. Joe's worst fears were confirmed, the hot fire which had fallen through had distorted both the pan and the ashpan door.

"We've got to block the gap where the fire's dropping through. It's our only hope. We could lose other bars if we're unlucky, they could melt." Tom was almost reduced to a sombre silence. He hummed and erred. Then responded suddenly to a suggestion made quietly by the attendant Kettleness platelayer. "C'mon son," he grabbed Joe, "Get yuh coal 'ammer, an' a bucket. Over to the platelayer's cabin, back there." Obediently, Joe followed without question. The ground near the sleeper-made cabin had a domestic cast iron wash-house basin built loosely into a firebrick construction. The space beneath the basin showed traces of past fires. After a few words the firebricks were gently pulled apart and in moments they were on the cab floor of 9881.

"I'm goin' t' show yuh now," emphasised Tom West. "There'll be no charge for this lecture and demonstration. Just imagine that you're in the Mutual Improvement Class."

The fire-irons were lifted into the cab from the side tank-top. The fire was removed from around the missing firebar and the newly acquired firebricks broken into suitable, but quite large, pieces. "Now watch this. You pick up the piece I point to and put it on the shovel." Without much difficulty he bridged the offending space with the firebrick pieces leaving just sufficient space between to allow air to circulate. "Now, coal'll burn on there an' nowt'll fall through int' t' ashpan, save ash."

As the train and engine rattled downhill through the tunnels with everything under control, Joe and Tom busily washed their faces and hands in the engine bucket in an effort to make themselves respectable for their silver-screen debut. The scene on the square cab footplate was like an image conjured from Dante's Inferno. Black shiny tunnel walls flashing by and shafts of dancing firelight picking out two shadowy figures as they worked amid the smoke and dust.

The downhill run required little steam, within minutes they could see the distant, tiny speck of light at the end of the tunnel. They rolled noisily and quickly towards it, Tom West let the loco run fast and free while he gesticulated and shouted to Joe. "No one need know? Keep it t' yerself. There's alus somebody who'll say it could've been done another way."

"What about Charley?" shouted Joe. "Don't we tell him?"

"Bloody Hell! I forgot all about 'im, good Lord! 'e 'as to make a report t' the Loco Superintendent." The circle of light at the end of the tunnel expanded and in an instant they were bathed again in bright daylight. "We should've brought 'im wi' us t' Kettleness. Hope the poor beggar's alright."

The train ran gently on towards Sandsend. The lush green landscape, the bright sky, the surface of the sea which rippled under the caresses of the gentle breeze, Whitby Town and its harbour piers, and the cliffs beyond capped with the splendid Abbey ruin; a naturally composed masterpiece about which a film director was to respond rapturously.

"Can yuh see anythin' happening Joe?"

"Some folks standing on the platform."

Tom slowed his train, he had an appointed stopping place. Joe knew where it was too, it was marked, the director would be somewhere close by.

"Get yuh 'ead out like 'e said. Try not to look like long faced cow." The two cameras, uniformed rail staff and a couple of extra's dressed as holiday camp red coats were casually placed, talking and busying themselves and awaiting the arrival of the 'campers'.

The motion of the train ceased when Tom decided. He'd been given a mark by which to stop and that was where he was going to stop. He, not the director knew when he should brake. Tom did, he applied his full train brake at the moment he assumed correct.

"Within a quarter of an inch," Tom proclaimed. "See, that stop mark. No, its an eighth of an inch. I knows me job, eh 'undred percent Tom they call me." He and Joe beamed towards the assumed notables, at the cameras and especially the female red coats. The crowd shuffled down, cases, kids, with dads and mums, noisy teenagers, some with smiles, others glum, but all acting like a crowd heading for a 'Holiday Camp'.

An interview dialogue absorbing a few people was being conducted and filmed as others left the station by the exit. "That's Flora Robson." Joe called loudly to anyone listening.

"Not right yet lads." the director was heard shouting. Tom and Joe strained to hear what he meant. "We'll have to do another take," He waved at the extras who were still disembarking. "Back in, it wasn't good enough. We need more action in the shot. It was lifeless, dead. The engine was lifeless." He turned to address Joe and Tom West as they looked out from the cab. "That was a bloody lifeless run. Can't you do better than that?"

Tom was completely taken apart by that comment. He blew and snorted. He gobbled angrily, spluttering to find words in defence. 'Misinformed, bloody railway expert, is he? Daring to bloody criticise me.' Tom's face expressed the thoughts that formed in his mind.   ·

So volatile was Tom's exasperation that his upper false teeth were humiliatingly ejected out of his mouth. He snatched out instantly to intercept the flying upper dentures but missed. He was normally the expert 'fielder' in this situation, and his past successes would raise mocking cheers and applause from his shedmates. Not this time, his field of catch was limited by his presence in the engine cab, he couldn't be expected to dive out of the cab and catch his teeth in mid-air.

An obliging hand shot up from the small crowd and caught the teeth in flight. Caught them at the moment they were about to disappear over the side of the platform and fall in between the rails. The obliging hand threw them back, but not without comment. "These teeth want cleaning. There's bread and cheese on 'em." Tom fielded the throw and disappeared momentarily into the privacy of the cab to replace them back in his mouth.

The laughter had barely died away before Tom returned to the original upsetting remark and shouted clearly back at the director, "Course it was a bloody lifeless run, it was down hill."

"We'll have to do the run again," said the trilby-hatted director with total authority. Then added emphasis in a way of responding to the startled look still etched across Tom West's face. "Yes, do it again."

"I'll come up this time Tom." The voice belonged to Charley, the York locomotive inspector whom Tom and Joe had earlier left behind. Charley Brown placed a foot on the steps leading up to the side tank locomotive and struggled to climb aboard the engine.

"Back the train out of the station," Charley instructed. "And back up 'till you're out o' sight behind the retaining wall, then come like a bat from 'ell wi' chimney smoking, steam blowing from every cylinder cock, safety valve blowing off, an' use the whistle. Mek it clear that she's in action workin' damned 'ard, as if she's pulling the train into the station."

"Bloody phoney that's what i' is. It won't look like a real train."

"Course it will. You'll mek it Tom, I know yuh of old."

"If I do what you've just said, we'll come down that 'ill like the bloody runaway train, an' she'll blow, an' she'll blow. We'll jump the rails about 'ere and plunge into the beck. The water'll sober yuh up before the train flattens yuh into a splodge o' raspberry jam."

"Use yuh brake, yuh engine's steam brake. On second thoughts use yuh 'ead, it'll be better than a brake when it's on the line, it'd even stop the mighty dreadnought."

"Fancy telling me 'ow to drive an engine. An' then telling me 'ow to do it wrong. Bloody insolence." Tom mulled it over audibly as he prepared to propel the trainload of passengers up the single line. "He'd better do this wi'in the rule book."

The time allocated to them to occupy the section between Kettleness and Whitby West Cliff was quickly expiring. The temporary firebox repairs and the heated debate about Tom West's driving had devoured valuable minutes. They had to make speedy progress because in thirty minutes the next scheduled service train from Castlebrough was due to use the line. Fired with an enthusiasm born of his irritation caused by people 'who didn't know what they were talking about,' Tom made the locomotive accelerate efficiently, keeping it's feet firm and noisily propelling the five laden passenger coaches up the incline towards the tunnel.

The guard and the locomotive inspector stopped the moving train with the vacuum train-brake handle in the guardsvan. At the required moment the train moved forward and down the incline. Tom West blew the engine whistle long and hard, Joe caused steam at a pressure of 175lb per square inch to escape noisily from the safety valves and made the chimney emit a billowing mixture of black smoke and white steam.

"Haven't you forgotten something they asked for mate?" asked Joe.

"No." With that reply Tom promptly opened the cylinder drain-cocks. They blew hard and loud with even staccato spurts of high pressure steam ejecting in synchronisation with each full revolution of the driving wheels. Tom West's train entered Sandsend platform with the noisiest show of steam and smoke that the station had ever witnessed.

"Hope they're bloody well satisfied," Tom splurted out accompanied by defensive moves around his mouth in case his false teeth wanted to find another resting place.

Satisfaction reigned all around except in the engine cab. "I 'ope no one knows that I'm driving this engine," said Tom. "Otherwise when the film's shown a' the cinema I'll 'ave t' resign, I couldn't bear the disgrace."

The director appeared with Charley Brown alongside him. "Smashing that was, we got a great shot. Thanks a million mate, an' you fireman."

Charley interjected, "Cheers Tom, me ol' mate, sorry about that but yuh knows what these film luvvies is like." He cocked his head in the direction of the director who was walking away. "Anyway, yuh times up, the service train'll want to be through soon. Look us up in York sometime, an ah'll buy yuh a pint."

"Better mek that a bloody barrel, mate, an' don't yuh go telling anybody about me driving the train wi' me brakes full on, or I'll have yuh strapped to buffers on a coal train."

"All aboard," shouted Joe. " We can go, the guard's waving us off."

"Tarrah, Charley," Tom and Charley squeezed hands. "You're a crazy locomotive inspector, yuh know that." Tom winked and grabbed the whistle cord. A shrill blast rang out and the regulator was gently opened. Charley stood on the platform end and waved the pair off as the train eased into forward motion.

On to Whitby West Cliff, then to Castlebrough and Filey. "We're going t' get away from crazy locomotive inspectors and film directors," Tom emphasised with waving arms and fierce facial expressions "We'll say nowt about the driving down hill, wi' the brakes on! With - the - bloody - brakes - on," he emphasised. "I can't believe it! In this day and age, nowt about somebody buggering up the firebars. You understand," Tom asked. "Agreed?"

"And the teeth, don't forget, say nowt about the teeth," said Joe loudly intending his remark to be humourous to lighten Tom's mood.

The homeward coastal journey was unhampered by anyone. Southwards within sight of the gently heaving sea, through Whitby West Cliff Station, and over Esk Valley. It soothed and quietened the angry Tom.

The magic of the hard climb up the 1 in 39 from Robin Hood's Bay prompted Joe's creative literary thoughts again. He recalled Fifty Bob's story about a local author called Leo Walmsley who loved and lived in the area through which they were travelling. He had created a mythical 'Bramblewick' which replaced the reality of Robin Hood's Bay. 'What must it be like to be a writer?' the thought often inspired Joe.

The even beat of the three cylinder locomotive paced him as he swung his shovel to fuel the hungry conflagration that roared in the firebox. 'He was on top of his job' he assured himself, the burnt gasses discharging evenly, almost hypnotically, from the chimney head showed just the correct colour. His skill pleased him. These days he was not often troubled by the 'camel's hump' problems that dogged his early years as fireman.

A good day, good weather, good exciting company, he should be on film somewhere. He glowed with satisfaction. He looked across the cab, Tom looked relaxed now too, the earlier aggravations and humiliations of the day must have finally deserted him.

Back at Filey Town they waved to the extras, the crowd actors, that disembarked. "Like leaving old friends. Seems like I know them all now."

Castlebough Motive Power Depot welcomed them only by its familiarity. The yard was quiet with little activity from the locomotives stabled there. 9881 was propelled into number two road and after damping down Joe and Tom climbed down and headed for the messroom. Joe almost felt as though there should be a welcoming party for the fledgling film stars but no one mentioned their film making trip. At least not until they entered the messroom with its sole occupant, Johnny Marsay.

"Had a good day then?" queried Johnny. The conversation drifted on and Johnny revealed that he had heard on the shed grapevine that a re-take would have to take place next week, it was definitely not a wind up he stressed.

"A retake! What the bloody.....," Tom clasped his hand firmly over his upper lip, turned and disappeared through the messroom doorway.

"Yeh," Johnny shrugged. "Apparently the light wasn't right for the shot, or summat."

1
England`s Last Hope

A dark mood overshadowed Joe's natural optimism and humour. He wasn't exactly sure why. One moment he ascribed it to the jostling and mickey-taking in the messroom earlier that morning. Then he would lay the blame for his mood on Carol. He'd seen her walking down the main street hand in hand with an unknown youth. Although he hadn't seen Carol for almost a year, it had made him feel alarmingly jealous, almost angry.

Then there was the added worry of having let the fire die on engine A8 1985 for Hull Goods. He felt such a fool. 'After all', he silently rebuked himself, 'I'm a fireman employed to keep fires burning and what did I do? Let the damn fire go out on Ankler's engine, only ten minutes before he was due to leave the shed'.

His thoughts came back to the present and he shrugged slightly, not so as to be noticed by the other three passengers; it was more a symbolic shrug to throw from his spirits the growing black shadow that threatened to envelop him.

The early morning Castlebrough train on which he travelled towards Malton battled against the snow and wind. He could scarcely see through the compartment window because of condensation on the inside and driving snow on the outside. Dawn had effectively swept away the shadows of the night but daylight could scarcely pierce the shrouding effect of the falling snow.

"Have a look son!" said a man on the facing seat, clearly aiming his remark at Joe. "See what your Labour Government's doing to the country. More shortages and more unemployment than during the war."

Joe reached forward to take the offered newspaper without comment. 'He's smartly dressed,' thought Joe. 'Not a labourer or coal shoveller. Manager maybe going to the city for a day's work in some posh office. Then home and as clean as ever.'

The fellow handed the Daily Mail to Joe and drew his attention to critical articles that told of strikes, food shortages, electricity cuts, and coal at pit-heads that couldn't be moved because of the state of the railways. He pointed with satisfaction at large headlines, 'Red Government in Crisis,' it said. 'Cabinet Resignations Expected.'

"An' they had the cheek to march into Parliament after their election, singing The Red flag, I tell you, singing The Red Flag. It fair boils my blood."

added the man's companion on the next seat, stabbing his pipe-stem in Joe's direction.

"What does? The Red Flag?" Joe's first words broke out almost unexpectedly and displayed his irritation. "Why are you picking on me?"

"Because you've got the damn cheek to wear that bolshie badge." The pipe-stem stabber punctuated every word deliberately. He leaned over towards Joe to examine the badge. "Worker's of the World Unite, that's what it says Arthur. It's commie."

Joe pounced back. "What else does it say?" demanded Joe leaning forwards and pushing his lapel badge closer towards his tormentor. After a slight pause he continued, "N.U.R. That's what it says. National Union of Railwaymen. It's my trade union badge. The union believes that the workers should unite." Joe's irritation showed clearly and the two smartly dressed passengers seemed well pleased at rousing him from his early morning stupor as if to provide some sport.

The Mail reader resumed his line of attack. "Seeing it, the Red Flag I mean, and hearing it being sung fair gets my blood on the boil. You listening Jack?" he asked addressing Joe. "I saw a young fellow once flying a Red Flag from his engine. He was an insubordinate little so-and-so. Proper cheeky little sod. I told you about this in the office didn't I, Harry," he said to his neighbouring passenger. "I insisted on the sack for him. But his union brothers created. That's what they call themselves, Brothers. He'll never do it again, even though I let him off."

Joe suddenly recognised the man as the L.N.E.R. shareholder who'd had him disciplined about the red flag on the lamp bracket over a year ago. Cautiously he buried his face in the large pages of the 'Daily Mail', removed his cap and placed his reading spectacles on his nose. 'Thank God I've got reading glasses to hide behind,' thought Joe, even though he was secretly bothered about anyone knowing that he needed glasses for reading. It was obvious to Joe that the man didn't have a good memory for faces so he gradually became bolder as he read the Daily Mail. Caution was abandoned when one of the other occupants commented strongly about the proposed nationalisation of the railways. Joe took the bait and contested the other's opinion by delivering a spirited defence of the Labour Government.

The clatter of wheels on rails as the express sped towards Malton provided a noisy background to the verbal duel that Joe now confidently promoted. He was arguing for what he believed in. He had to remain polite, as an L.N.E.R. servant he couldn't argue with a passenger.

The rapiers flashed, Joe parried all thrusts and found plenty of targets with his own weapon. He felt pleased and comforted himself with the conclusion that his adversaries were really very badly informed about current affairs.

The train's forward motion was suddenly slowed and the passengers showed their alarm at the immediate retardation that the train exhibited. "The brakes are going on wonder what's up?" the pipe-stem stabbing passenger declared.

"Just a snowdrift," Joe said calmly as if to offer some comfort. "We're through now. We're doing about sixty and it'll take more than that bit of snow to stop us. There, that's Rillington."

"I'll be leaving you at Malton. Just when you gentlemen are all on the ropes," Joe announced loudly with exuberance. He made a mental note that he'd changed from his duelling metaphor to a boxing metaphor. Had he mixed his metaphors he asked himself? The question prompted him to draw his trade union postal course from his pocket for confirmation. The subject of the most recent lesson had been the use of metaphor and simile to aid expression.

With his adversaries now talking amongst themselves, Joe took the respite to recall the confrontation in the messroom that morning which had resulted in much mickey-taking. He'd proudly made public reference to his postal course studies and the expectation of a week long course at Oxford's Ruskin College.

"Yuh'll go daft wi' reading," Bill Clarke had boxed the side of Joe's head for emphasis. "An yuh 'air'll drop out."

"Yuh don't care if yuh eyes drop out, do you Joe? yuh can allus sell matches," Alf South had said, punctuating his cryptic remark by joining in the collective guffaw.

"Your only nineteen. Leave politics for au'd geezers. Time tha was rooting after lasses," Bill Clarke had added more to the baiting game.

But the mickey-taking had changed tack when the sound of heavy boots scraping across the sand strewn floor caught everyone's attention. "Yuh've been sat on, ain't yuh Wade, we' yuh finger stuck in an 'ole somewhere," Jack Mild had shouted loudly. "Yuh've let the bloody fire go out on the Hull Goods engine. An' Ankler's on for it in fifteen minutes."

"I'll go and light it," Joe had said thoroughly demolished by this final piece of public ignominy.

"I know you will. I'll see to that," Mild had added with conviction.

"He's bin readin' the Dandy," chimed an onlooker.

Joe knew that he was in error. He had just spent an hour preparing Ankler's engine for the road and he'd never even checked on the state of the fire. He didn't totally despair. He knew what to do. Diminish it's importance, divert attention, that was the strategy.

"Yuh must o' peed on it Jack. It were alright when I left it." He had then deserted the scene of his verbal harassment and with a bucket of paraffin and an armful of cotton waste to get a fire going again. The hot firebox vapourised the paraffin almost immediately and it started to smoke vigorously. Joe had then tossed a handful of burning cotton-waste into the vapour-filled fire-box and nimbly side-stepped the flame blow-back that shot from the firehole door.

When Ankler's engine had pulled out of the shed into the early morning darkness with thick black smoke oozing from the chimney he'd felt relieved. He'd become even more delighted when Bill Clarke told him to travel on the cushions on the the the 8.10 am York express to Malton for a few hours work at Malton shed. Clarke had said that the shed staff there were depleted in numbers by the rapid spread of influenza and the problems caused by the recurring ice and snow of this stark 1947 winter.

"You're goin' as England's last hope. We expect you t' do your duty." Bill had presented a mock salute. "Get lost in a snowdrift, the deeper the better," Bill had concluded to the mocking accompaniment of others.

"Aye, an' tek yuh books, wi' yuh."

Why everybody had been so blinking jolly at seven o'clock in the morning, in a smelly, soot-laden atmosphere, laced with cigarette smoke and various body odours had posed a query for Joe. They would creep about the filthy confines of a barely lighted shed with naked flame paraffin torches for light, either cleaning, oiling or repairing locomotives. Why were they so boisterous and always desiring someone to torment?

"This looks like Malton." declared one of the passengers in the compartment. Joe returned from his recollections of that morning. He handed the newspaper back to the traveller facing him.

As the train approached Malton East signal cabin the snow crunched under the wheels slowing the train's progress. "God! It's snowing like Hell," Joe exclaimed as he viewed the outside through a tiny patch of cleaned window that he'd diligently produced. He lowered the vertical window and thrust his head bravely into driving snow.

The locomotive shed on the left of the train and the expanse of track-bed displayed little human movement. The flat terrain carrying the rail-track towards York was only visible for a few hundred yards. In the distance a few stooped figures worked away to keep the points and signals clear of snow.

"You aren't going any further. The lines are blocked at Castle Howard." The voice was directed towards the locomotive crew as it drew the Castlebrough train alongside the up line platform. Joe heard the message too. He turned inwards from his open window and spoke to his travelling companions.

"Lot o' snow laid down since we left Castlebrough. That chap shouted that the train won't be going far as the lines blocked at Castle Howard."

"Better get off the train, both lines are blocked in four places," said a porter to Joe as his carriage drew to a halt. "You'll be warmer in the refreshment room."

"I'm sick as hell of this," grumped one of Joe's travelling companions. "I've already lost three days work in the office this year."

"You can't blame the railways. It's this bad winter, worst for years," returned Joe.

"We don't have any coal," interrupted the railway shareholder angrily, "and that's the Government's fault. All these power cuts. Wouldn't have happened if the old warrior with his cigar had won the election. There is no damned coal. The Labour Government is useless."

Joe didn't respond this time, he pulled his cap down tightly onto his head and with his coat-collar upstanding he left the compartment and ploughed his feet through six inches of virgin snow. He glanced backwards down the platform and saw the Castlebrough train with it's compartment doors thrown open and moving figures streaming from it.

Joe approached the engine shed as quickly as he could struggle through the biting wind. "Hello there, son." called a shadowy figure from within the gloom of the small two-lane locomotive shed.

The bright daylight and snow dazzled Joe as he focused on the figure, its tallness and its bulk conjured up echo's of familiarity in Joe's subconscious. Then he discerned the figure's large floppy cloth-cap. "Big Ted Coney?" he shouted and then addressed him properly with some show of apology. "Ted, I didn't mean to use your nickname. You remember me Ted?"

"No, don't know that I do."

"Yes, Ted, we dropped our plugs at Ravenscar," added Joe thinking that this reminder might produce recognition in Ted's mind.

"Get in 'ere out o' the snow lad. Mebbe I'll see yuh better."

Joe struggled against a sudden gust of wind and driving snow. "I mean when I dropped the plugs Ted, at Ravenscar. On the snow ploughs. With the doctor on board, two years ago, remember?"

Big Ted laughed and belted Joe between his shoulders. "Didn't recognise yuh kidda," he paused and pointed down the shed in the direction of the time office. "There down there, you've got t' go there t' sign in. As I was sayin', didn't recognise yuh, aye, it's two years since we took them bairns t' Whitby. In the ploughs, got a letter I did, saying what good work I'd done."

"I didn't get no letter," added Joe feeling vexed. Then slipped into introspection about his own use of the unnecessary double negative. He'd have to watch his Yorkshire dialect, he didn't want to become careless. It was alright speaking in a rich dialect but quite another to be using the English language wrongly.

"Yuh was only the fireman, son. Anyway yuh was left behind at Whitby t' get some overtime in." He grinned down into Joe's upturned face. "But yuh did well. Yes, I remember, it were you, that dropped the boiler plugs on that J21."

"Was it?" Joe queried snappily but left the subject and stated, "They're short of men here. They've sent me over to help out."

"Half the shed down wi' flu an' t' other 'alf missing in snow."

"Snow ain't that bad Ted. At least it's not blown about much."

"Not 'ere it hasn't, but then there's only been about four inches an' it ain't drifted. On the Wolds it's a different kettle o' fish."

"Not in there, Ted." A voice from behind halted their progress, it was Jake the time-office chargeman. "You an' the lad's wanted up at Burdale and Driffield."

"What for?"

"Call it snow shovelling. Call it icicle breakin' in Burdale Tunnel if yuh like. Got engine 1581 for yuh in the Whitby bay platform. It's the eleven o' five dodger to Driffield, the early train were cancelled, so there might be a bit o' fresh snow to get through."

Big Ted was back at the time-office door within five minutes. "Thought she were ready, yuh said. There's no bloody coal in t'ole. Can't expect us t' get t' Driffield and back wi' on'y a coal scuttle full of coal."

"Course yuh will Ted."

"How d' yuh bloody know. Yuh ain't a locoman, Jake."

"No, but Swalesy is, an' he says yuh'll have enough t' get through t' Driffield."

"We're not just goin' t' Driffield, we'll be bringin' the dodger back to

Malton, yuh silly git,"

'Was Ted feigning anger?' Joe asked himself. He was certainly going to town on Jake the acting running foreman.

"There's a couple o' wagons o' coal at Driffield that yuh can bring back t' help us out."

"I ain't goin' wi'out some more coal." Ted Coney meant it and Jake just had to make a concession.

"We've got 'alf a wagon o' coal Ted, to last us, Tek a bit more from that."

"Yuh scrapin' about a bit. If you're pinchin' coal from Driffield."

"We are Ted. There hasn't bin a coal train this way for three days. Some sheds are cancellin' trains 'cos they've no coal."

"Yuh'll have t' cancel the dodger this morning then, I ain't tekin' 'er out."

"Chrise! Ted. Go an' get a bloody tub o' coal."

"Two tubs?" Ted replied. Jake turned away without either hearing or commenting on the request. He was off into the smoky dark depths of the loco shed.

Ted was to ignore his instructions. At the coal stage Joe, using the steam operated crane, hauled the first of three square tubs up above the engine's coal-bunker. Three tubs taken from the solitary wagon very nearly removed all of its coal. The small G5 locomotive simmered quietly but displayed wisps of steam blowing from every gland and joint. It was heavily laden with grease and dirt. Ted Coney continued to mutter complaints, "It shouldn't be on the line. Goin' t' shops for repair that's where the bloody thing should be goin'."

Joe was glad to climb down from the cab roof where he had perched precariously in the wind and snow manhandling the swinging coal tub. It was no easy job extracting the catch at the side of the swaying tub and then inverting it so that its contents fell into the loco's bunker. "Ted, I'm bloody glad we don't have this method for coaling our engines at Castlebrough. Even wi' out this weather it must be difficult."

"Yuh gets used to it," Ted replied. "Nowt to it."

"But you're a big fellow, Ted. You'd never get up there."

"Course I can. It's the knack. Yuh've just got t' get t' know it. We alright for water?" He didn't pay any attention to Joe's answer as he climbed the side of the locomotive and pulled his bulk through the tight door space. "Let's get crackin'. Let's 'ang on t' train, an' get up there."

2
No Water at the Tap.

To Joe, 'Up there,' was the high point of the line, the summit at Burdale Station, some ten miles down the line. Joe was not familiar with the line from Malton to Driffield, he had never travelled it. The railway authorities didn't consider it necessary for firemen to know the line before they fired locomotives over it. The driver, on the other hand, had to know every change in gradient, every signal, siding, gate house, speed restriction, as well as any recent changes that had taken place on the track. He was expected to instruct his fireman on how to respond to the route. Joe would only know what might be around the next corner if Ted told him what to expect.

"Sod of a little bank comin' up," Ted shouted across the closed cab. "Then straight into a cuttin'. Keep 'er topped up wi' steam. I'm goin' to mek 'er crack." Joe responded that he was alright and the engine was steaming well. "Yes, but there'll be drifts," Ted answered.

Sure enough his forecast proved correct. They hit a two-feet drift about ten yards long and quite suddenly all forward movement ceased.

Ted Coney screwed down the hand brake. "Come on son. We'll shift some of this if we move smartly and catch it before the wind changes." Through the cab doorway Joe watched the wind swirl the snow around in flurries. But Ted was out of the cab with a broad-bladed platelayer's shovel in his hands in a flash. Joe followed him down the steps to find that the guard was already there as well. Two passengers came to help with only a piece of fencing available to them in lieu of a shovel but they soon surrendered and sought refuge back in the train. In a short while the locomotive's wheels were cleared, her smallness made her liberation easier. She moved off again slowly through the cleared pathway and struggled up the gentle gradient towards the first station on the branch.

Settrington station was a tiny affair and looked a picture postcard as they pulled in alongside the snow-covered platform. The station staff were awaiting their arrival. Their train of two passenger carriages and three vans squealed to a gentle halt. Ted and Joe looked out of their locomotive back down the length of the train.

Ted began an explanation, "These 'ere vans, they are full of provisions, food and things for some of the villages on the Yorkshire Wolds, Thirty-ton of foodstuffs. Some of the Wold's villages have been cut-off for two weeks."

At the roadside the locals awaited delivery of the provisions with sledges, hand-carts and horse-drawn farm vehicles. "No coal." Joe heard the train guard shout to the locals. Their collective groan was easily audible above the blast of wind and snow. A few passengers left the train and labelled provisions were loaded onto the sledges and carts for delivery to outlying hamlets and farms. Activity ceased and the guard's green flag and whistle instructed Ted and Joe to continue their journey.

Similar calls were made at North Grimston and Wharram, up five miles of rising gradients they climbed but avoided being halted again by snow-drifts.

"Glad we got three tubs, son. We're burning a bit. That lout back at the shed had no idea what we'd burn, ploughing uphill through these drifts."

"It's getting steeper, Ted. What's up front now?"

"Burdale bank, an' then Burdale tunnel."

"A tunnel? Ted. You didn't say."

"I'm sayin' now. Burdale Tunnel, its a mile long but downhill in this direction."

"Downhill you say, so we've still got to get over the summit?" Joe asked

"Don't panic son. You've plenty of coal and water."

"Hope so," replied Joe, his mind full of memories of his only other trip with Big Ted Coney through Ravenscar tunnel, a much shorter tunnel than Burdale Tunnel. "We're burning a lot of coal. You're having to drive on a low cut-off," he added, almost as if apologising to Ted for the reference to him driving on a low cut-off.

"Got to. This snow an' wind makes even this little load 'ard to pull."

The small firebox was fiercely consuming coal to efficiently turn water into steam. He fired carefully intending to burn the smoke off the newly charged fire before they entered the tunnel. Joe took time aside to wash his hands and drew some hot water into the loco's bucket. This was something he wasn't doing just lately. The harsh winter, the rough work, the constant abrasions caused by the firing shovel and coal handling had left his hands with sore gaping wounds. He opened the cold tap on the coal bunker front to add water to the boiling water already in the bucket.

"No water at the tap, Ted." he shouted above the noise of exhausting steam and clanking con-rods.

"Why not? Is the tap blocked?"

"No."

Ted Coney's head was out in the driving snow looking for a level crossing. He drew inside briefly. "It'll be blocked. Check the water gauge."

"I have," replied Joe again checking the tank water-gauge to see at what level the water escaped from the perforations. "We've got about a quarter of a tank left."

"That can't be." Ted left his engine controls and operated the gauge and the tap. "She was full at Malton, wasn't she?"

Joe took the question to be a statement of fact. "Was she? I don't know?"

"You never looked! Yuh mean, yuh never looked. An' I asked yuh."

"Bloody hell." Joe was showin' his teeth. "It wasn't my job to check the tank was it?"

"I expected that yuh'd 'ave checked the tank when yuh were up on top coalin' 'er up."

"Not bloody likely. I was at one end tipping them ancient, bloody square tubs into the bunker. I ain't got six bloody legs and elastic arms." Joe demonstrated that his earlier timidity about fighting his corner was disappearing in favour of a more aggressive defence.

Ted didn't respond directly to Joe's outburst. "I'm sure Sharpy said the engine was ready for us. Must 'a bin, 'ow else could 'e 'ave expected us to tek it out."

"He knew it was short on coal. Anyway Ted, we ain't finished yet."

"What's that supposed to mean? Course we are finished."

"No Ted, I was thinking of melting snow in the tanks."

Ted looked quizzically at Joe. "What a crazy idea." he exclaimed with a guffaw, "We'll need a couple o' thousand gallons. Are you goin' to scoop it up in yuh cap?"

Joe felt humiliated and fought back. "Better than dropping your plugs."

Ted gave Joe a queer squeezed-up look with his wrinkled face. "They're your plugs. I don't drop plugs. You're the fireman," he stressed, without any change of sentiment. Joe couldn't help but wonder whether Big Ted was joking or whether he'd forgotten their time together at Ravenscar.

"We're goin' up a stiff gradient, for 'alf a mile. Then down through Burdale Tunnel. We'll 'ave t' stop at Burdale Station just past the quarry and take stock." Ted closed the discussion.

'They hadn't better blame me for the empty tank,' Joe emphasised to himself. 'I just do as I'm bloody well told.' He vowed to himself to keep his boiler full. That way he'd be in a better position if the tank ran dry.

The snow refused to halt its steady downfall and the wind showed no sign of abatement. The small G5 locomotive pounded up the hill with its depleting water reserves. The drifting snow curled in at either side of their passage as they noisily hauled the short train into the cutting and on towards the stone-portalled entrance to the tunnel. They had a long way to go. The chimney top blasted out the exhausting steam as Ted thrashed her into action. 'He must be neurotic about tunnels,' thought Joe. 'He flogged the engine to death through Ravenscar tunnel. I'm sure I could make a better job of it.'

He stuck his head out of the cab behind Ted and saw the problem they had to surmount. The approach to the tunnel was preceded by a long cutting which by accident rather than design caught the snow carried by the prevailing easterly wind. The cutting, indeed the whole line had only been kept open by the repeated passage of light trains, but nature had a way of confounding the plans of men and today looked like a perfect example, newly formed masses of snow were being sculptured by the wind into beautiful flowing shapes. Joe marvelled at the designs of nature, and marvelled again at the way his versatile, rugged little locomotive kept biting through the clinging mass.

The coal and the water disappeared relentlessly as the unequal struggle went on, but so did the distance to the tunnel mouth, The huge limestone blocks that the masons had so carefully shaped and placed to form the piers and the portals came tantalisingly closer. Snow, deposited high up on the bank above the tunnel mouth came cascading to block their final assault to the entrance.

"Oh 'ell. Pull the sands valve on. I'll need all we've got t' break through." shouted Ted. The regulator was wide open with the valves on a very low cut-off, the exhaust blast roared so powerfully it could have expelled some of the working parts. The snow clutched at the front wheels and muffled in around the front end. Ted surrendered to the struggle and quickly closed his steam regulator. Before Joe could meaningfully compose a possible query, the steam regulator valve was suddenly wide open again and the four driving wheels and connecting rods spun wildly at the in-rush of steam. He then repeated the strategy, urging the train forward.

'She'll founder Ted,' thought Joe. 'Keep her going, making her slip'll just stop her.' But darkness suddenly fell, the loco found it's feet on the snow-free lines inside the tunnel. The chimney barked evenly against the tunnel roof. As more and more of the train broke free from the grasping folds of snow the easier the task became. Ted's tactics had worked, the engine speed was increasing.

"We're in," shouted Ted, "but keep yuh 'ead in, there's icicles hanging down." They were running downhill now.

"We're through. That's for sure now, Ted," shouted Joe.

They gathered speed and raced downhill with the steam shut off. Nothing should stop them now as they plunged into the soot-dense blackness. The firelight picked out the angular lines of the cab and marked out the area of their existence. Ted's big face was moonlike and high in the cab, it shone down on Joe and presented a beam of satisfaction. Snow, coal shortage and even the low water level in the tank had temporarily gone from their concerns. Joe stepped across the cab to comment approvingly on their progress. He moved to shout upwards into Ted's ear and at the same time looked through the round spectacle window. The words stopped in his throat, instead another message emerged. "Look Ted, look, a red light."

Ted seemed unable to move. A still photograph stood in Joe's mind, rather as it had done when the trains crashed at Castlebrough. He felt the words well-up to be shouted again but Ted was now reaching for the brakes with a remarkable slowness. Or so it appeared to Joe. But then, the reality registered and the still photograph melted into a blur of action, revealing that Ted had moved with the speed of escaping steam.

The brakes were biting, Ted slammed the reversing lever into backward position and put steam pressure into the cylinders causing the wheels to spin backwards. The crew froze, the imminence of the expected collision riveted their attention forwards through the circular spectacle window. The red light disappeared from view. "It's a train's rear lamp. Christ. hang on." Joe clung to the cab side, still craning through the window. They held tight for what seemed like an eternity until the engine finally ground to a halt. There was no collision. No bang or crash, only the noise of the engine gently hissing and wheezing as if expressing its total oblivion to any potential danger.

"The light's here, Ted," Joe's words shed relief on the feelings of sheer terror that the two were experiencing. But no sooner had he uttered the words and the engine's water injector failed sending a roaring blast of steam out into the tunnel. Joe moved quickly and closed the steam feed. The noise abated but the red light still hovered motionless in the blackness.

"Get a torch lamp Joe an' tek a look, you'll be quicker than me."

With the comforting circle of light from his paraffin torch flickering in front Joe picked his way towards the obstruction. His gaze fell first on a battered boot and then on a train tail-lamp. As he slowly moved the lamp, he discerned a human shape, in heavy grimy clothes, slumped in a tunnel safety recess.

Joe was startled and stumbled back to his engine. A constant drip of water from the tunnel roof fell across his shoulders. He hurriedly reported to his driver. "It looks like an accident, a bloke, I reckon he's been there some time. He must be frozen to the bone."

"Is he dead?" asked Ted as they both returned to the victim.

"Gawd, I don't know, think he's breathing." replied Joe as they stooped for a closer look. The body obliged with a groan and a leg moved.

"It's Wilson, Ernie Wilson," explained Ted Coney. "What you doing Ernie?" There was no reply. Ted shook his shoulder gently and he groaned again.

"He's frozen Ted. Can't we get him into the guardsvan?" The train's guard had appeared on the scene.

"On the footplate makes more sense. Warmer. He needs warmth." Ted stooped, grabbed Ernie's shoulders and heaved him up. Joe climbed up the cabside and the three of them together manhandled the limp body into the cab.

The guard's face looking questioningly from the darkness was eerily illuminated by the flickering light of the naked paraffin flame. "Get back t' your van and gi' us the whistle," Ted mouthed at the guard. With Ernie's belongings on board they drew away on the guard's signal. Joe heaved Ernie into a sitting position in the corner of the cab taking care to protect him from hot steam pipes.

"The tank's dry," Joe bellowed into Ted's ear. Ted nodded, he'd heard the injector fail and he knew why. The half-full boiler would take them through the tunnel Ted reckoned. They urged forward into the blackness and the half mile run down to Burdale.

"Ernie looks bad. Must 'ave bin there through the night," Ted looked at him. "Hope there's a doctor."

"Who is he, Ted?"

"An odd bod you'd say. A tramp perhaps. No 'ome, came from no-where. Says nowt, 'as nowt, so they say. Fred Jasper gives 'im odd jobs t' do on 'is farm and lets 'im live in 'is 'ayloft. Proper lit'le 'ome and bed. Only thing 'e ever talks about is the Mons battle an' 'is long lost twin brother."

Joe had little to do except pray that the boiler water lasted through the tunnel. He didn't relish having to throw the hot fire out in the tunnel, that's what he'd have to do to avoid blowing his boiler plugs. The Ravenscar episode returned hauntingly to his thoughts. 'It mustn't happen again,' he swore to himself. He really would be taken off the footplate, there'd be no excuse this time, he wouldn't be able to blame Ted Coney again.

The boiler water level bobbed lower, Joe managed to stop the engine blowing off steam by using his damper control. Relief flooded through him when Ted shouted. "There's light. The end o' the tunnel's coming up."

They burst back out into the blizzard again. The metallic screech of rail against wheel was muffled by the deep snow that sought to halt their progress. Ted opened the regulator wide and the engine barked loudly and defiantly, he was desperate to reach the platform.

The deep drifts, which camouflaged the different levels of the rail and platform again grasped at the wheels and the engine's motions. Ted and Joe toppled forwards and clutched the nearest obstruction for safety. The stubble covered face of their unconscious passenger slumped over and he slid bodily across the cab floor.

"This bloody snow," gasped Ted. "Bloody mountains of it, we're still not at the platform." He looked back down the train to see a few passengers straining to see what was happening. Ted opened the regulator gingerly, so as not to spin the wheels, and, as if by a miracle the train crept forward folding back the glistening white shroud of snow until they were safely at the platform. "Thank God!" Ted exclaimed as he wound on the hand brake.

3
A Medal for the Royal Train

"Boiler's low, Ted. That's worrying me," said Joe emphasising the urgency. Ted's only reply was to give a long loud blast on his engine whistle. Its intended role had been to attract attention but human forms were already emerging through the snow. The unresisting figure in the engine cab, now showing slight signs of life, was hurriedly bundled by many willing hands through the cab-side opening and into the teeth of the storm.

"Take 'im t' the booking office, we've got a fire in there," instructed the station master. "We'll soon dry him out. What happened?"

The station master's query went unanswered. "He'll need a doctor or first aid," Joe heard the train guard insisting. "He's got a busted ankle. I think."

Joe now turned his attention to other considerations, he ought to remove the engine's fire, he pulled the long iron shovel into the cab, nervously looking out for the return of Ted Coney. 'Ted should take the decision to chuck the fire out,' grumbled Joe inwardly. Just as he was about to start a coiled heap of hose pipe was bundled unceremoniously into the engine cab.

"Hang it on the boiler son. It needs thawing out," shouted Big Ted through the cab doorway. He pulled his cloth cap tightly onto his head as a sudden gust nearly swept it away. Joe obeyed and started to frame a query but Ted disappeared into the storm again before the query could emerge from Joe's lips.

Joe took the decision he'd been about to request. "No good chucking the fire out if he's going to get some water in the tanks. She looks as though she'll wait a bit," he muttered glancing at the empty gauge glasses. It was not long since the water level had disappeared. Ted Coney appeared at the cab side with a second frozen coil of hose and arranged it on the boiler.

"What we going to do Ted? Have you found a tap?"

"Yeh, the one in the lavatory, it's not frozen. They use these pipes t' water the station gardens, it should just reach the tank."

Joe settled easily when he the heard the slow trickle of water entering the tanks at either side of the loco.

"Hey son look at this," Ted reported he'd found a leak on the right hand cold water feed injector under the cab. "Reckon its bin leakin' badly all the way from Malton." Relief flooded Joe upon the realisation that the lack of water in the tanks wasn't a fault on his part. "Pass us the coal 'ammer, I'll fix it wi' elbow grease."

"It must have been leaking when we left Malton, Ted."

"Must've, anyway we didn't leave wi' an empty tank. It's been the leak." He started washing his hands and face when hot water from the injector became available and then said. "Well they're gettin' provisions off the train, they've got some food now." Ted carried on talking, he was not usually as talkative, but now he was relaxed and a little jovial. "They've taken the tramp, Ernie I mean, they've taken 'im t' that large house just down from the station. I'll be down there for an 'our or so. Yuh'll 'ave t' come for me if I'm needed." He disappeared into the falling snow and along the platform towards the station buildings.

Joe muttered to himself, "A bloody hour! What about me?"

A small gang of men appeared and started moving snow off the neighbouring lines. The falling snow had abated a little but the sharp wind kept the drifts on the move. Joe helped for a while and as he laboured, he learnt about the conditions on the Wolds. The line from Driffield to Malton had been blocked many times. Mountain rescue teams had been used to get food supplies through to Huggate.

"Yuh'll be 'ere for 'ours," the station master said to Joe as he entered the booking office room where the fire offered warmth.

"There'll be some passengers who've got to be taken on surely?" questioned Joe.

"How? In this weather, not a chance, there's on'y two, both for Driffield. They're in 'ere keeping warm."

Joe changed the subject. "Do you know where my mate is?"

"Course. Don't you?" grinned the little North country station master.

"No. Where is he?"

"Oh, I don't dig in other folks's cabbage patches."

"What?"

"I say again. Is yuh ears blocked wi' snow, lad, that tha can't hear nowt. I don't dig in other gadgies cabbage patches. Unless there ain't no weeds. Then I'll dig. You go an' do a bi' o' diggin in Ted's garden yerself."

"Ah's flabbergasted. Ah's Yorkshire cocker," responded Joe, doing his

best to broaden his own dialect, "But I daint nay what thah's a talkin' abaht."
"That ain't Wolds lingo kid. Yuh's proper lost up 'ere in these 'ere 'ills."
Joe was trying to answer, like with like, but he was no match for this
Yorkshire Wold's man born and bred. He may be wearing a L.N.E.R. sta-
tion master's uniform but he certainly didn't talk like one.

"I sez again, where's m' mate gone an' I don't want t' know about no
cabbage patches," Joe emphasised his change from broad dialect to clear
English. "Where has he gone?"

"Down yon road for about a quarter of a mile, on the way t' Thixendale,
there's a stone 'ouse. If it isn't buried in snow, yuh'll see it on the right.
Turn left down there, couple o' hundred yards, to the church and Ted's in
the stone house. He'll 'ave gone to see Irene, passion flower of 'is 'eart
she is."

"What at this time of day, What's he gone for, a late lunch?"

"Aye. That an' all," responded the station master with a cheeky grin.

Joe changed the subject. "More to the point. How long do you think
we're going to be here?"

"Days or weeks?" asked the station master, but answered his own question before Joe could gasp. "We're 'ere while someone meks a fresh road
through from Driffield end. The snow got real thick again this morning.
There's no ploughs available, they're clearin' the main lines. They'll 'ave
t' mek a clear route from Driffield as there'll be the kids t' get through
from school. Yuh'll just have to wait instructions son."

Joe returned to his engine where the solitude and the heat from the
boiler made the sheeted cab the cosiest place for him to be. It was another
opportunity which presented itself for him to study his postal course in
English Language. He prepared himself a brew from his billy can and
unravelled his notes from his overall's pocket.

Oh! why hadn't he gone to grammar school like his cousins had? He
would have loved to have been launched on the road to the fields of knowledge and go fishing in the sea of learning. He dreamed on in a peculiarly
productive thought stream. He had words which he must capture on paper.
He shuffled deeper into a comfy position on the fireman's seat and relaxed
and let a dream of being back at school envelop his thoughts. He closed
his eyes and with the aid of his vivid imagination he reached out for his
metal-nibbed pen on the big sloping school desk. His hand still stretched
out for the elusive pen. He pushed hard at the obstruction to his outstretched
hand.

"Bloody nutter! What yuh doin'? I'm soddin' wet wi' yuh tea. Yuh chucked it at me."

'Was that his teacher?' His mind spun and he opened his eyes. Big Ted provided the answer as his tall figure stooped and picked up his sandwiches from the floor of the engine cab.

"Yuh was fast asleep. I was bein' quiet and yuh and chucked your tea an' yuh grub at me."

"Me pen," Joe started, and then consciousness opened him fully to Ted's obstructive presence and the sizzle of the engine.

"I wasn't sleeping, I was just restin' me eyes." The plaintive call of a cow in a nearby barn accompanied Joe's pleading. He commented about the cow being cold in a vain attempt to divert the critical eye of Ted Coney, but Ted stared on.

"I just called back t' check that all was in order. station master reckons we'll be 'ere a while yet, so I'm off back t' house. Gi' us a blast on the whistle when I'm needed."

The afternoon passed by quickly, surprisingly so for Joe, as he had spent much of the last few hours patiently awaiting some working instructions. The snow flurries had temporarily abated. It was now late afternoon and dusk was gently closing in.

A little apprehension concerning the whereabouts of his driver had crept into his stomach, so much so that for the last few minutes he had shuffled up and down the platform gazing at his empty train. He was at the far end of the station when he made out the shape of a small figure lurking about his locomotive.

"Hey you! You can't take any coal," Joe protested at the country lad boarding his G5 tank engine with an empty bucket, but the protest fell on resisting ears.

"Grandad Silas sez good footplate gaffers allus gi' some coal away t' cold folks." the heavily dressed youngster said.

"Tell 'im we don't," Joe's answer was straight to the point.

"We've hardly no coal at 'ome mister. We've got little kids an' grandad living wi' us."

"Sorry, I've been told not to give any coal away. Where do you live?"

"You'll 'ave t' come down tiv our place. Meet Grandad, he's near 'undred years au'd. He'll tell tha abaht working t' expresses up t' Great Northern line wi't old spinners. Drove Victoria, on the Royal Train an' got a medal. He'll tell yuh more than yuh thought existed."

"Hundred you say? Can't believe that. Folks don't live that long in places like this."

"Come on down tiv our 'ouse. See me Grandad. An' the kids. We've got some grub." Joe shook his head, but he was curious about how much this young lad seemed to know. "Tha knows the engine gaffer, off this engine, 'e comes t'our 'ouse, 'e's thar now."

Joe listented intently, he was about to enquire further but the young lad continued. "Me Auntie, she'll be in bed wi' 'im, keepin' 'im warm."

"What!" exclaimed Joe with disbelief, "In bed with her, at it, you mean, at this time of day, with his train in the station." The young lad didn't answer, he just held a grin across his face. "The randy begger, I wondered what he was getting up to. Where is he now?"

"In big 'ouse."

"Yes, but which big house?"

"Tha don't know nowtt Mister, tha must come from a long way away. Tha don't e'en speak proper," the youngster was doing his best to annoy.

"Cheeky little sod. Show me where footplate gaffer is."

"Have telled yer. In big 'ouse, our 'ouse."

Joe dismissed the insubordination from this 'damn cheeky little monkey' as he thought of him.

"Tha's a funny one Mister, tha is a mister ain't yah?"

Joe ignored the lad's questions. "Where is my engine gaffer?" he insisted carefully pronouncing every word.

"By Gawd, Mister, I'm cawd. Ol' Coney's keepin' warm wi' me auntie, as I said."

Joe decided on a more conciliatary approach. "Let's get on the engine. I'll give you some coal."

"Thanks. Fill the bucket mister, then I'll take yuh to see me grandad and ol' Coney."

The rectangular big house with an angular ridged-topped slate roof silhouetted sharply against the evening sky was large by comparison with the agricultural buildings of the Yorkshire Wolds. Joe found himself in a large living room.

'A blinkin' palace really alongside the houses of the workers.' Joe thought. 'Scruffy, but it's got carpet up the stairs and that's Ted's pipe on the mantelpiece.' He moved over to inspect it more closely.

"What's that to thee son?" A voice from within a large armchair stabbed into his conscience and made him feel like a nosey parker.

"It's me mate's," replied Joe startled at the sight of an old man totally enveloped by the armchair.

"Tha means yuh Gaffer, don't tha. Yuh footplate gaffer, the Cap'ain o' yuh ship. Call him what tha wants, he's yuh gaffer. 'is pipe's alright on t' mantle piece. Mind tha neb," he said tapping his nose.

"Where's tha from, young un?" asked the man as he selected another wooden pipe from the mantelpiece on which Ted Coney's pipe rested. He picked up a length of already rolled up newspaper and used it as a taper to light the pipe.

"Castlebrough," replied Joe politely, even though he detested being addressed as 'young un'.

"A towny eh. Tha knows the smell o' the privy, but not the fields, or flowers in t'edgerows or the tang o' an 'orses arse end." The old man punctuated his words with a chuckle.

The discourse was not on Joe's terrain, so he changed the subject. "The lad who brought me here said you were a Great Northern driver of the spinner's on the expresses?"

Pleasure and a friendly glow spread over the old driver's parchment-like features as he responded slowly and clearly. "Not the Great Northern, the North Eastern."

"You drove the royal train, the lad said. What was it for? Why you?"

'Cos Me Da' an' 'is Da' drove royal trains, so I 'ad t' do t' same, in the family, it is. We're a royal train family." He chuckled again. "Why d' yuh think we got this grand house. It were gi'en to us as a reward for Royal Service."

"Wow! Crike! Being given a house like this." That was Joe's astounded response. He paused and followed it with the question. "Did Royal trains come up here? Up this little line!"

"What's tha mean little? This line goes ti London and ti Fort William. Yuh can't go no bigger than that. My Granda' was at York locomotive shed. 'e took Queen Victoria and 'er Albert to Castle 'oward in 1854. This picture shows 'is train at Castle 'oward."

The old man proudly exhibited a framed 'Penny Magazine' featuring a litho-print of the Royal Train at Castle Howard station.

The conversation came to an abrupt stop as a distant engine whistle screeched and the thinly glazed 19th century windows vibrated. "Just come through the tunnel. He'll a come for yuh two." Joe guessed that 'you two' meant him and Ted.

"Where is Ted," enquired Joe.

"He'll be 'ere in a mo', when 'e's finished," the young lad had reappeared and responded. With that, a heavy thud sounded in the room above, followed by the sound of heavy boots on the stairway. Sure enough Ted appeared in only his cap, shirt and underclothes. He grabbed his pants off the big brass fireguard where they had been hanging, unnoticed by Joe, and dragged them on over his boots. His face looked remarkably clean. His eye's settled on Joe.

"Yuh should be on t' engine, I told yuh to stay put. There'll be no coal left in the bunker."

"That whistle, Ted, it's somebody else's. It weren't our engine."

"Tha hopes so," Ted's irritation showed strongly at this intrusion into his private life.

4
Seven to the Rescue

The distant engine whistle produced a string of urgent blasts. Joe hurried out through the door using the opportunity to escape Ted's scathing tirade. His boots ploughed through the fresh snowfall as he raced off towards the station and the unknown engine. The sounds of the visiting loco carried on the wind and its outline loomed out of the darkness.

"Crikey there's three," Joe exclaimed. Not one, but three coupled locomotives from Malton shed had arrived.

One of the drivers shouted in Joe's direction, recognising his locoman's attire, "Where's yuh engine mate?"

"Up t'other end," shouted Joe in reply. "Beyond the stock."

The Burdale station master labouring through the snow behind Joe called out to him. "Get yuh driver an' 'ang yuh engine on to these three others." Joe pointed at the rest of his stationary train and opened his mouth to make a remark. "No, leave the stock," the station master anticipated his question. "You're all goin' light towards Driffield."

Ted Coney was still lumbering up the road, not yet in Joe's sight. The engine was more important to Joe than Ted's immediate whereabouts, he knew his fire and boiler pressure would be low by now and that he'd better do something about it quickly.

The station master relayed the news to the assembled loco crews. "The afternoon train from Driffield t' Malton is stuck fast between Fimber an' Wetwang. There's school bairns on it. It was banked out o' Driffield wi' three engines, but still got stuck."

Joe was embarrassed now, he was holding up a rescue mission. He worked fast and furious with his shovel to raise enough steam to allow their journey to commence.

Joe coupled his G5 to the other locomotives and the entourage set off in the direction of Sledmere and Fimber Station. The engines each carried local men in the cabs for help with any digging out. The initial falling gradient from Burdale favoured their journey towards Fimber.

Conversation in the crowded cab discussed the weather. "Reckon it's worse than last Saturday when they got the mountain rescue team to tek food an' stuff up to 'uggate village."

"Aye," agreed Ted, "Silas wuh tellin' me its worse than in t' Alps."

"Roads blocked all over Yorkshire, ten foot deep in places, busses off, Goods train stuck on Speeton Bank, wi' another behind 'im."

"They shouldn't 'ave let train leave Driffield, they should've known the line were blocked."

"We'd 'ave been better with a snowplough. It's deep Ted."

"Reckon there ain't none spare. Keep yuh fire right. Don't let 'er blow off." Ted instructed.

"Not much chance of that, the way we're fighting the snow." Joe replied. "Looks like we'll need all the coal and water that we've got."

"Just coming up to Sledmere and Fimber," Ted yelled. "Watch out for the home signal."

"Some hope mate, sky's filling wi' snow," shouted a platelayer riding with them in the cab.

"Blast it," cursed Ted as the coupled engines hit a drift about five feet deep. "Nearly stopped us," he yelled.

The snow easily gave up its grip against the sheer power of four coupled engines and they surged on.

"Boards on Ted." Ted noted the stop signal and gave a long blast on his engine whistle. The other drivers replied and all the locomotives slowed. A man at the trackside grasped the handrail on the slowing G5 loco and heaved himself up on the steps. He was the local platelayer, acting as fogman today. Heavily dressed for the occasion he squeezed his way in through the cab doorway.

"Better in 'ere," he declared. "Must be bloody minus ten outside."

"Any news? asked Ted of the fogman as the locos halted at the signal. "Will we get the train out easily?"

"Nope, not yet anyway, loads o' drifting snow, an' its starting t' come down like merry 'ell again." He pushed further into the already crowded cab. "We'll 'ave t' do a bi' o' digging."

"Best go and tell the other crews,"

"I'll go," instructed the fog-man only to be diverted by a knock on the driver's side cab door. The face of the Fimber signalman appeared in the gap.

"Train's about a mile ahead, jus' passed crossing keepers 'ouse, if you get that far. Ah'll go an' gi' yuh the road." The signalman vanished as quickly as he had appeared and after a short while the signal was pulled off to the all clear position.

Ted Coney's response was a long blast on his engine whistle

which received an acknowledging blast from the trailing engines. "There's kids stuck on that train. About twenty five, bin there four hours already." Ted displayed an unexpected concern for the occupants of the stranded train. He would usually express uncaring attitudes or display a brutal lack of sympathy. Joe suspected he was a more sensitive man than he would admit.

The storm was going to determine their tactics, that was soon realised by the engine crews and all concerned. They made slow progress but inevitably closed the gap between them and the train they'd set out to rescue.

A forlorn looking train stood grounded in the snow. The locos at either end were smoking gently as if unhurriedly awaiting the arrival of help. The carriages themselves were unexpectedly deserted. Signs of life drifted from the crossing keeper's house which had been requisitioned to provide a sanctuary for passengers and schoolchildren. They lay scattered about the floor of the main room in the tiny building.

The engines coupled to the train engine. The drifting snow which had earlier trapped the train was shovelled to either side of the track. In what seemed no time at all in the circumstances, the passengers were led back to the train and helped to scramble aboard. The youngsters were in remarkable spirits despite their ordeal.

"Seven engines for this short train, you'd think it'll shift now," Joe shouted above the noise of the departing train. The engines roared their determination into the wind, driving wheels spun wildly and hot coals and sparks were thrown skyward.

"They will." said Ted.

"We're away!" Joe yelled, as the train heaved forward.

"She's off, gi' us some steam," Ted Coney shouted excitedly. The anger that had boiled in Ted earlier at Silas' house, at the unwanted intrusion into his private life, was now forgotten.

"Best I can do." Joe yelled back. "Not a lot of coal left." His shovel searched around in the blackness of the small coal bunker to find only slack and dust. "Okay for watter though," he shouted and demonstrated to Ted Coney.

The unusual train formation arrived safely at Sledmere and Fimber station where parents, hot soup, tea, biscuits, cakes and porridge awaited everyone. They crowded into the station's buildings full of relief and glad of the refreshments. Later, some left to attempt their way home, others remained, having decided to spend the night and await daybreak before finishing off their journeys.

It was well past midnight when the train rolled back into Burdale. The falling snow had at long last ceased and the night sky was clear.

The waiting room lights still burned and Irene welcomed the train crews. Irene, Rene or Reen, depending on who was speaking to her, was strong and tall, nearly equal to Ted, but with a mature figure which hinted that she'd been an attractive country lass in earlier years. She wore plain functional working clothes and blended easily into the Wolds environment and its people.

News of the old tramp, Ernie Wilson, filtered through when Ted and Joe entered the room.

"We thought he were a goner, Ted." Irene said holding close onto Ted's arm. "We couldn't get any help. We'd tried Doc Richardson at Huggate, He couldn't get here because of the roads were cut off."

"Where is Ernie?" Joe asked.

"At Silas's house, our house," Irene replied. "There's an army lass with him. Knows what she's about, blood pressure, temperatures and things. She found an empty whisky bottle stuffed in his coat and reckoned he was just drunk, fell asleep in the tunnel. There were no bones broken."

"What d'yuh think 'e were doing in tunnel anyway?" asked one of the Malton drivers.

"Tekin' a short cut, I'll bet," said the station master. "I 'eard that Ernie'd been cleanin' out the cellars of the Mason's Arms in North Grimston on'y t' other day. Landlord had said he'd gi'en 'im a bottle o' best Malt instead o' wages. Au'd Ernie would've used tunnel to get back 'ome. Going o'er top in this weather would 'ave been impossible on foot."

"Yeh, that sure sounds like our Ernie." Ted said, "he'll be alright then, when 'e sober's up."

Burdale was only ten mile's away from Malton by rail, mostly on down hill gradients. The short train stormed through the snow and the drifts in the direction of Malton Station. Joe's cracked hands, covered in chaps and sores burnt and stung. He showed them to Ted, hoping for an expression of sympathy. Ted's response was to say 'Snap' and display his own weather wounded hands and face.

"Ted, it's nearly twenty-four hours since I booked on duty this morning," Joe said as they both looked into the face of Ted's pocket watch at five a.m.

"Since you booked on yesterday morning you mean, not this morning. It's Tuesday now tha knows."

"Crike," said Joe, "I'll get about three days pay for this shift."

"You'll get more because some of your hours will be paid for at a higher rate," Ted explained.

"That is, providing I can get home from Malton when we get back there."

"You'll be alright. The York mail train'll be running to Castlebrough by now." They rattled through a sleepy Settrington station. "You'll soon be home." Ted said

"You'll be home before me."

"I can't be?"

"Course you'll be home before me. Where have you got to go?"

"Burdale."

"Burdale." echoed the startled Joe. "You've got to go back to Burdale?"

"Aye."

"Why's that then?"

"It's me 'ome where I live, wi' Reen. O'er brush we are. Didn't yuh know Reen were me wife. I popped 'ome for a bath whilst yuh were at station, Yesterday."

Joe was dumfounded, "Oh, I thought....," he started and then decided to keep the thought to himself.

1
The Red Nose Society

The four night-shift cleaners improving the cosmetic appearance of C7 Atlantic locomotive 2992 at four o'clock in the morning were far from enthusiastic about their duty. The sudden cold spell in April after the snow had cleared made them lazier and less like work than usual. Huddling . close to a lighted brazier they smoked cigarettes for comfort and shivered. The cold and the frosts in April had made them demand a fire to work by.

The 1947 winter had been very harsh. The record snow falls had been followed with flooding over huge areas and hurricane winds, all of which had left much destruction in its wake for everyone.

"Four o'clock in the morning, and we're slaving away," moaned Willie Wagget. "It's worse than the bloody army," He usually wore an eternal grin on his face and was ready with a joke on his lips, but not this morning. He grumbled on, "Bet Frobisher's asleep in front of 'is fire in the store. We're too young t' be out of bed at this time of morning. Night work for under eighteens, is banned, isn't it?"

Willy was overheard by the running foreman. "That was for children," Frobisher said, his presence entering their circle of firelight from out of the darkness. "Mind yuh, yuh aren't old enough to be children are yuh. An' Wagget, by heck you've got the right name ain't yuh, You're allus bloody wagging it."

"Wagging what Bill?" Alf South saw chance to gain Frobisher's side before Wagget could respond. "What's he been wagging? What were yuh wagging Willy? Oh I see, Willy, you was wagging it again!"

"Gentleman Alf South, chirpin' in when he should be minding his own business," said Frobisher, emphasising his sarcasm. "He's getting very uncouth of late, if this carries on it'll mean he'll be saying bad words like 'heck' and 'blooming' soon."

"Smacky bottom, smacky bottom, now then Alfie," a fourth voice chipped in. They then all laughed in sympathy with non-swearing, non-drinking, Alf.

"Eh," Wagget was on the offensive now. "I'll get our kid onto you." He was now intent on getting one up on Bill. "Actually he's not our kid, he's me cousin. Yuh know him Bill, Bruce Woodcock, the European heavy weight champ, he's me cousin on me Mam's side."

"Lying git," Bill Frobisher muttered. He turned to examine the engine in the light of his naked flame lamp. He expressed intense dissatisfaction with their work, he used the most disgusting words he could summon. "This engine's got to be on the 8 am Leeds, spick and span, and off the shed thirty minutes early to steam-heat the train," Frobisher looked worried. "I've bin told that Macclesfield the millionaire racehorse owner is on the train to Leeds, an' he's an L.N.E.R. shareholder an' all. Yuh might remember, if there's out about yuh, he complained last week about the state of the train."

The cleaners didn't listen to Frobisher's concerns, they were still discussing the first subject of conversation.

"He's kidding you now, Bill?" said Alf. "Woodcock isn't in his family, Bill."

"No he's not spinning a yarn, Bruce Woodcock really is his half cousin, Wagget's Mother's sister, Jessie, married Bruce Woodcock's brother. That's right in't it. The big fight's in two weeks. Woodcock and Joe Baksi, the American heavy."

Wagget swelled with pride but the others either didn't notice or didn't care.

"Who are yuh backin' then Bill?" asked Alf, directing the conversation onto the forthcoming big fight.

"Me," Frobisher paused. "A fiver on Baksi, I reckon."

"On the Yank against a Yorkshire man. My relation an' all. Yuh traitor!" charged Wagget. "Woodcock'll slaughter Joe Baksi. I'd back that anytime."

"Is he that good?" asked Frobisher. "I thought, I was told....."

"Yuh don't know boxing, Mr Frobisher, keep yuh money, don't go backing fighters. You're a racehorse specialist, aren't yuh? Me, I'm so sure I'd put ten pounds on Woody, never mind your measly fiver."

Frobisher turned away. "You haven't got five pounds to your name sonny!"

"He's running now," quipped South, "That's why they call him the Running Foreman."

"You're on," snapped Frobisher, now determined not to be outdone by his subordinates. "Here's my fiver, I'll give it to Mason for holding. Get yours out." He shook Willy's hand fervently.

"I didn't mean it," Wagget stuttered, totally taken aback by Frobisher's overbearing confidence.

"Course yuh did, give your fiver t' Mason, he'll hold it. You're not just a big mouth, are yuh?"

"I am," replied Wagget trying his best to wriggle out of the situation.

"An' I'd taken yuh at you're word? What yuh messin' about at?" Frobisher's face moved so close to Wagget's he could smell his breath. "I'd accepted your offer. What if I'd cried off? Eh!"

Willie didn't move, he couldn't move, but his mates egged him on, pushing him over the edge. "Yuh's got to mean what yuh say in betting." urged Mason, "Yuh ain't got no standin' if yuh backs out, after you've stood a bet."

"Yuh took his bet Will. I heard it?" Alf shouted, he wouldn't normally be seen betting but gave into double standards on the grounds that humour was his justification.

"Come on William, up! Pay up, or your name'll be mud when Woodcock loses." Frobisher's outstretched hand emphasised his determination.

"He ain't, he ain't goin' t' lose. You're going to regret this," Willie said bravely counting out five pounds in coins into Mason's hand. "Yes," he muttered. "I've wagged it today, ain't I. Hope no silly beggar tells our lass?"

"I will," Alf South said jovially, Mason readily agreed to do the same.

Frobisher, having regained the respect of the lads was now in a charitable mood. "Come on, take a break, into the messroom an' get warm. Have a cup o' tea."

Bert Woodley and Joe Wade signed on at six thirty in the morning to take 2992 to the station for the eight o'clock departure. The messroom was alive with activity, cards were flying and first, as well as second, breakfasts were being prepared or consumed. The discussion over the 'big fight' and Bruce Woodcock was still being hotly debated. Wagget and Frobisher both knew Woodcock and had once visited his little 'gym' in the back garden of his house in Doncaster. They knew him to be unspoilt by his success. The working class lad, turned heavyweight boxing champion, was soon to fight Joe Baksi the big ex-miner from Pennsylvania for a chance at the World title.

Joe Wade was back into boxing too, his enthusiasm rekindled by the 'boxing fever' sweeping the country. He'd even taken to sparring again. Jim Packet, who worked at the shed, was a tough ex-marine and fought semi professional bouts, he'd persuaded Joe, one night after a round of drinks, to join him in the rear room of his Auborough street house for some 'training'. Jim was in the messroom too and eagerly participated in the conversation.

"Baksi's a mountain of a man," Packet said. "But he can't beat Woodcock. He's too slow."

"Yep, I agree, Woodcock's got a right hook that's just like a whack from a swinging firing shovel."

"Hey Joe," Frobisher had cornered Joe. "Who do you think is going to win the World title?" He asked as Joe and Bert sat down.

"Woodcock," There was no hesitation on Joe's part.

"Oh, Why?"

Joe elaborated about Woodcock's style and strength so eloquently that Frobisher felt the wind drop from his sails.

"Well I'm backing Baksi," he reasserted himself. "I always put me money where me mouth is."

"You'll lose it. Woodcock's got the talent of a world heavyweight. He could beat even the brown bomber, Joe Louis, Baksi's tough, but not fast enough. Yuh'll see."

"I won't see," came back the foreman. "Yuh'll see. I've got a fiver on it that says you're wrong. A nice new white fiver. Same colour as white feathers. Yuh know about white feathers, Woodcock's had some sent."

"Tek the bugger on Joe. I 'ave," encouraged Wagget. "He's throwin' 'is money about. 'e'll be skint. Mason's holding the stakes."

"White feathers. We'll wait and see whose got white feathers." He took five separate one pound notes out of his recently collected pay packet. "I'll double me wages this week. Let's have a slip?"

"I'll tek it for yuh Joe," promised Mason. "I'll keep it safe."

Frobisher was now well and truly upstaged by his subordinates. He had to regain control of the situation, after all, he was the boss. "Right then," he tapped the face of his watch. "You two, get yuh selves up t' station wi' 2992. Get the train warmed, if millionaire Mack's on that train, I want it right, D'yuh understand. I don't want no more complaints comin' back." He drew breath in readiness for his next tirade but was stopped abruptly in mid gasp.

"Get this out." Jack Lambert, the chairman of the L.D.C. was frantically tapping the glass on the official note case. So intense was his agitation that silence descended in the messroom. "Somebody ought to be sacked over this" he bellowed.

"What's up, mate?" One of the engine cleaners shuffled across to the notice case and peered in. After a brief moment, a chuckle emerged from his vocal chords the silence broke.

Almost in turn, the occupants of the messroom gradually gathered around the notice case and a growing laughter steadily erupted.

'If the nose fits. Wear it' was the heading on the unofficial piece of paper pinned to the board.

> Teddy the Red Nosed driver, has a very, very shiny nose,
> Those who've seen it in the dark, swear it really glows,
> All of the other drivers used to laugh and call him names,
> They never let poor Teddy join in railway games.

> Then one very foggy Christmas Eve, Franker came to say,
> Teddyo with your nose so bright,
> Will you guide my train tonight?
> Then how the unions loved him and they shouted out with glee,
> Teddy the Red Nosed, driver you'll go down in history

> Red Nose Society

Jack 'Teddyo' Lambert absorbed the intention of the unofficial notice and decided that a humorous response was now the best reaction. "Bloody clever eh, good, good," he squeezed the end of his nose and grimaced at the assembled workmates. "An' I thought it were blue enough to hang outside the cop-shop. Still, its good to see some initiative out o' yuh bunch a bloody loafers. One day yuh might just make reindeer herdsmen. Yuh'll never," he emphasised, "never ever become train drivers."

2
Another Little Gamble

Locomotive number 2992 of the famous Atlantic class, looked cleaner than she'd appeared for many months. Wagget, South and Mason had performed a remarkable task. Frobisher must have threatened an unusual sanction to make them turn the engine out so smartly.

'A mighty machine of extraordinary power,' mused Joe, awed by the size and length of the three cylinder, four-coupled gleaming locomotive. He conjured up expressive images to clothe her in magic and exalt her beauty and strength. Her sleek lines, her smooth curves, her prodigious bulk, she was the utmost transcendent embodiment of sheer power and majesty.

The early morning office workers and others had yet to join the train as Joe clambered about the locomotive and arranged the pipes to flush steam into the carriage heaters.

"The coal needs trimming!" Bert's bland remark echoed in the cab and was enough to instruct Joe to climb up onto the coal and level it off, making it safe to travel at high speed without any falling off.

"Yes I'll do it now." From his vantage point on top of the engine tender solitary passengers could be seen joining the train. One of the distant figures reminded him of Carol Blanchard. He hadn't seen her for a long time. He looked more intently and recognised the woman, 'Yes it's her, it's Carol." He climbed down the steps at the rear of the tender and emerged onto the platform in time to see her disappearing through an open door into the the train.

He couldn't comprehend why she had seemingly drifted out of his life. A closer friendship had seemed on the cards, but that was nearly two years ago and it had come to nothing. He entered the corridor-coach train and walked slowly along the interior. The internal sliding doors were closed and the train was still quite empty. As he approached a smoking compartment he heard the sounds of subdued laughter.

A surprise awaited him in the guise of a male figure dressed in a heavy army greatcoat. Joe gasped, as next to the soldier figure Carol was seated, her attention was absorbed with a search in her handbag. Joe stepped back quickly to avoid the fellow's gaze or Carol catching sight of him.

The soldier was a big chap. Joe had no inclination to challenge the broad-shouldered service-man who sported a smudge of Carol's lipstick on his cheek. A tinge of jealousy swept through Joe's heart and mind and he escaped quickly along the corridor and out onto the platform.

It was a subdued Joe Wade who climbed back aboard his C7 Atlantic and with barely an acknowledgement to Bert Woodley, he vigorously fired the boiler, then swept and slaked the coal dust.

"Didn't yuh 'ear? Are yuh deaf?" Irritable questions that made their ways into Joe's ears.

"What?"

"Yuh talkin' t' dog's dinner or summat? Or are yuh talking t' yuh driver?"

"Sorry Bert. I was thinking."

"Stop thinkin' kid, it'll be the death of you. Have a chew o' baccy and stop thinkin'. Are yuh listening?"

"Yes," replied Joe.

"Well millionaire Mack has just been up while yuh was chasin' rainbows. He gave me a fiver, that's a quid for you mate, and four for the chief, me."

"A quid for me!" Joe exclaimed.

"Yeh, I'll give yuh yours now." he shuffled money in his palms looking for enough coins to make up one pound. "It's out of 'is winnings, what he'll pick up when Baksi beats Woodcock."

"Joe began a defence of his hero. "Bruce'll...," but then gave up and took the pound. Bert gave him another pound and then said, "Give your fireman two pounds if you like. Your both doing a good job. That's what he said," added Bert.

"Thanks mate. Maybe we're in luck today," Joe said, now somewhat mystified.

Bert practised his disgusting baccy-juice habit, he spat a mouthful into the firebox and then said, "He's got another fiver for us if we get t' York in fifty-seven minutes, stop t' stop, fifty-seven minutes. If we lose time for any other reasons, gates signals, suicides, you, name it. We've got t' pick it up again. Stop to stop."

"Can we do it, Bert? Means knockin' three minutes off."

"Yuh do the stokin' an' Admiral Beaty's mate'll do the rest. Get ready. Two minutes and we're off to break the record."

Every trick that Bert knew about locomotive operation was brought into action. The dry sanding system was used to aid acceleration as they reacted to the signal from the guard. The driving wheels didn't slip.

"Sailor Woodley knows what he's doing," he grinned. "Watch this, we'll be in York in fifty-seven minutes. I'll take another bet if yuh doubt it?"

Joe grinned in return and checked all the semaphore signals from his side of the locomotive. "All off and clear on this side Bert. What we got on?"

"Ten corridors and a horse box for Malton."

"That'll hold us up Bert. Are we dropping the horse on the platform?".

"The pilot engine at Malton'll take the horse-box off. We'll hardly know its gone."

The firebox was much longer than Joe usually experienced. The problem for him was placing the coal at the front end without hitting the brick-arch with his shovel. Being too careful and he might end up with another 'camel's hump' directly beneath the arch.

"All boards off mate," called Joe. He gave a wave to Jingo on the coal pilot in Washbeck Yard. The Hull pickup goods was waiting on number one independent ready to follow Joe's express as soon as the section cleared. Bert pipped the whistle and waved at the driver as he passed.

"Old Ben McDowd that, been driving since nineteen hundred and five, he's seen a change or two."

The locomotive rode evenly, she was noted for her good steaming and smooth running. Joe was absorbed in the thrill of the race against the clock. Bert shouted out his passing times as they flew by landmarks, cabins, crossings, bridges. He had his own unwritten programme of passing times which he'd compiled from years of service. "Thirty seconds up our sleeve," he shouted across the cab. "Thirty seconds in front, in three miles."

'Couldn't be,' Joe thought but didn't break from his firing task to question his mate. The safety valves sizzled as the steam pressure needle danced around the one hundred and seventy-five pounds pressure reading on the circular gauge. The old C7 had probably done millions of miles since she first turned her wheels on steel rails.

"She runs like a singer sewing machine." said Joe loudly to Bert who nodded and opened the regulator a little more.

She was flying along, no better image than flying described her achievement for Joe. His addictive response to the speeding run on the 4-4-2 Atlantic deminished other concerns. The brilliance of the April morning sunshine, which had just dissipated the last hint of ground frost, put them both in the right mood for a fast run.

Joe expertly 'shot' a covering of coals around the brightly burning fire bed and looked immediately at the chimney head to check the amount of discolouration mixed with the exhausting steam, he knew when his strategy caused the right combustion result by the amount of each discolouration. If she threw out black smoke Joe would know he'd overdone it and combustion in the firebox would not be at its optimum.

On past Ganton she flew, the vibrations of the heavy wheels on the rails passing shudders through their bodies as they touched close to seventy miles per hour. Crashing noisily over gate crossings, zooming under bridges, whooshing through stations with whistle blowing as they passed.

In no time at all they shot through Rillington station. The cross-rails and check rails groaned and creaked at the rushed invasion on their trackbed.

"Give him the money Barney. Give him the money Barney." Joe mimicked Wilf Pickles, the contemporary radio star. "Two and half minutes early. If old Mack knew what we knew he would never have wagered his riches."

Malton East's distant signal was at caution, reflecting the time-tabled stop they were scheduled to observe. Bert suddenly expressed annoyance and slammed his fist down on the metal fire screen. He turned to Joe. "What have I been bloody thinkin' on? We're early into Malton but we've got t' wait for the time-tabled departure time."

The train glided to a braked halt, a rushed application of the vacuum brake, but handled with a skill that stopped the train's motion without any strain. The horse box was shunted off as expected.

Off again! The thrill of the chase was upon them. The green flag, the whistle, the engine driver's reply, the 'Boards off mate' and the plop of the snifter valve all simultaneously heralded the pull of the mighty pistons. The first exhaust beat ejected a torrent of power through the chimney. The rhythm of beats converged and the brute force of the mighty atlantic pitched into forward motion. But was the race against the clock to be of no avail. Past Malton West signal cabin with customary waves exchanged, then to Hutton's Ambo and over the River Derwent. On around the curving tracks through Castle Howard and Kirkham Abbey stations. Then on to Flaxton for a fast straight run into York.

Joe straightened from his balanced firing position at the sound of Bert's call. "Did you look at the P.W. notices in the case?"

"Sorry no, I didn't. All that talk about Woodcock, an' red nosed Teddy, made me forget. Why?"

"There's a bloody caution on at Strensal. Ten mile an hour, half a mile o' new track." A string of foul words left his agitated mouth, words quite unsuited for public ears. Bert was waving his weekly booklet that advised train crews of changes in signalling and speed restrictions. He hadn't just read of the speed restriction caution in the book, he'd known since the beginning of the week. It had just not crossed his mind when he'd accepted Macclesfield's challenge.

"That's bust it, then Bert," responded Joe as he stood alongside his driver looking at the booklet of restrictions for the week. The reaction from Bert was to replace 'bust' with a stronger more expressive word.

Strensal's distant signal displayed it's caution position the first indication of the forthcoming slow-down. The second indication was not far ahead. A yellow Caution Warning Board marking out the commencement of the caution and speed restriction. On the side a black cut-out number ten dictated the maximum speed restriction.

The Atlantic locomotive and train ran smoothly from the established track and onto the newly laid unballasted length. The fifty-seven minute target-run still influenced their actions. They still yearned to make every second count and arrive at York as quickly as possible. The engine and train bumped and rolled over the newly laid section as Bert pushed the ten miles per hour to the limit. He knew his speed was closer to twenty than to ten miles per hour, he knew also that without a speedometer his lifetime's experience was his surest guide. He drove faster than he knew he should, "Just another little gamble," he said softly to himself.

The engine exhaust with its steady even beat quickened as they drew the rear of the train clear of the new track. They still wouldn't cease in their attempt to cover the forty-two mile journey as speedily as possible. Their pulses quickened as the engine rhythms accelerated to a roar. They gathered speed and quickly were in sight of Haxby "Not far from the winning post at York," Bert called out clenching the fist of his free hand.

But the winning post was still some way off. The approach to York, was peppered with speed restrictions and amber warning lights. They edged slowly through the tree lined cuttings, across Foss Island junction and finally out across the steel bridge spanning the Ouse. At last they could see the winning post - the majestic curves of York station roof.

"You did very well driver, a very commendable effort." Macclesfield had appeared by the cab doorway. "Just a pity about the pee-way caution at Strensal."

"We couldn't do nowt about it." Bert grumbled, agitated by the fact that he'd been seen to fail. He grabbed the oil can. "I'm just goin' to oil the

right crosshead, she's usin' too much." Bert disappeared through the op-
posite doorway and down the cab steps onto the ballast.

"Oh, he's gone," said Macclesfield somewhat taken aback. "I wanted
to tell him how much more comfortable the train is now since I complained about conditions last week. It was a good ride," he nodded. "I
think it's a foretaste of what we'll see when transport nationalisation comes
in next year"

"I hope so Sir." said the surprised Fireman Wade, who had that thought
all the private railway shareholders, race-horse owners and millionaires
would be Conservatives.

"I'm very enthusiastic about the Transport Bill. It's about the total in-
tegration of road, rail and canal transport," he paused as if searching for
his next words. "I may be rich, but I'm a Labour man born and bred, a
socialist, you know."

Joe was quite befuddled. A rich socialist was a complete paradox to
working class Joe's political understandings. So he steered clear of the
issue. "I think Bert's at the front of the engine doing some oiling," he
explained to Macclesfield.

Joe had to turn back into the cab and close down the water injector.
When he turned back to face the railway shareholder he found him well
into the cab entrance. His hand was extended towards Joe. "I'll have to be
gone, give this to your driver." He handed over two unrolled white five
pound notes. "One for you and one for your driver."

"Why?" stuttered the incredulous Joe.

The guards whistle sounded. "I'll have to go and join the train, I'm a
betting man I bet on the horses, and lots of other things too, also the big
fight that's coming up," said Macclesfield. "It makes me a very good living."

"Two fivers. A lot of money," gasped Joe. "But I don't follow you."

"Everybody's backing Woodcock for the big fight. The odds are good."

"And?" started Joe, then paused for him to explain.

"But he's going to lose to Baksi, can't help it."

"He's not!" exasperated Joe.

"Oh, he will, he'll lose," Macclesfield paused. "A lot of money is being
bet on Woodcock being the winner, I'm laying the bets off with people."

"I still don't understand," claimed Joe.

Macclesfield changed the subject, "It's like this, you've shown that
sharpening the timetable up to fifty-six minutes, Castlebrough to York, is

possible."

"Did we do it in fifty-six minutes? gasped the astonished Joe.

"Take off the time-tabled wait at Malton, and calculate a figure for the pee-way caution, and you'll find it was less than fifty-six minutes."

"Yes! hmm, er, yes!"

Bert Woodley returned to the cab but there wasn't much time now to talk, the train was due to leave for the rest of its journey to Leeds. "Why were you so interested in us doing the journey in fifty-six minutes?" asked Bert Woodley.

"I had a bet on the outcome with a carriage load of other passengers. I ran a book on you too, picked up a hundred pounds from bets I stood on the train. You hadn't to know about it."

"A hundred quid," gasped Joe.

"Have you always been, like, a betting man?" asked Bert.

"No I was a fireman and driver on these things, and a bookies runner before. Then I got my own race horses. Set up on my own I did. Here, take another fiver. I feel as though you two did the real work."

The platform inspector punctuated the conversation abruptly with a loud whistle blast and an instruction to close train doors. The unusual millionaire left their engine cab and disappeared with haste through the first compartment door. Bert popped the whistle and opened the steam regulator. A characteristic snort from the snifter valve on the superheater header announced the start and the first whoosh of steam blasted into the void of York station roof.

3
Blood on the Canvas

The terraced house down Auborough Street was close by the old hospital. 'Sailor' Jim Packett danced lightly on his plimsolled feet in the small back room. He attacked his imaginary opponent vigorously with his clenched, bandaged fists. He delivered a right-cross to the head followed by a left uppercut, then stepped back quickly as if some invisible referee pushed him back.

Sparring partner Joe, tucked safely into a corner, started the countdown to ten and shouted 'OUT'. Sailor, threw his arms up and did a victory dance. Sailor's big fists and heavy shoulders had Joe's glowing admiration but they also filled him with fear.

'How the hell had he got into this situation?' The thought repeated itself in Joe's mind. It was boxing fever, Woodcock fever. Call it whatever, but it had a hold on every young man in Yorkshire who had a little bit of sporting instinct. Boxing was experiencing something of a resurgence in post war, austere Britain. It was Boxing fever that had persuaded Joe to become Sailor Packett's sparring partner and use the little back room of the dilapidated terraced house as their gym.

Packett was a railwayman but he wanted above all to be a professional boxer. "Get your gloves on Joe," he called out. "Gi' me four rounds."

"Be careful. Don't bloody well hit me with a right like that."

"Course not, me old mate. I've never 'urt yuh yet. Have I? Come on get me ready for tomorrow's fight. I know I can take old Wiltin' Walker tomorrow at York. Then the fifteenth'll see Baksi laid low, an' Woodcock as world Champ., mebbe then he'll fight Joe Louis." Packet danced around the room shadow boxing anything. "And Joe, you get your pro's licence and we'll both make the grade."

"I'm not quite so sure as you Jim," Joe replied pulling his gloves on to accompany his boxing shorts and shirt.

Their feet thumped like hammers on the rough floorboards. Joe sweated and punched, occasionally running into Jim's gloves. Jim didn't hurt him, but Joe hurt Jim. He threw a wild right swing striking him hard on the temple.

"Sorry, Jim. Didn't mean to do that."

Jim winced. "Come on gi' me hell, storm at me, gi' me, get me, come on." Joe chose to retire, panting away in the corner. "Gawd," Jim said glumly. "That was more like fightin' old Mother Riley than fightin' someone like Woodcock."

"I'm knackered mate," panted Joe.

"Your on early turn tomorrow, aren't yuh? Then we go down on the three-thirty to York. That's it, Joe, you're not fighting, so come on, look happy about it."

Joe dreamily answered, "Yes." He couldn't help thinking he was doing the wrong thing by getting into boxing once again.

York Racecourse teamed with interested spectators. All caught up and excited by Woodcock fever, but also hoping to see blood on the canvas. Yorkshire's young professionals came here seeking a road to fame. Joe saw blood, and it hurt. It hurt him to see Sailor, his fellow railway worker, towering and slow, taking hard punches from his slippery and skilled opponent. So good was the contender that he must have had Joe Louis as his trainer. Blood ran from Sailor's right eyebrow, his nose spattered out blood every time it stopped his rival's devastating punches.

Joe hated it. He hated the watching crowd, ecstatic with bloodlust, yelling for more cutting, more blood, more unbridled violence.

"Stop bloody knitting yuh two."

"Stop cuddling him, yuh great puff."

"Go on, gi' him a kiss."

'Yeah', greeted every destructive blow that bloodied Sailor. Joe winced as he suffered each blow in sympathy.

Joe recalled how he had sworn to Jim that he would register as a professional. 'As soon as Woodcock finishes Baksi off,' he'd said. But now he felt sickened at the thought.

In a sudden flurry the referee stopped the bout. A deafening cheer for Sailor's opponent rang out. Sailor had lost.

"I'll have t' come and live down here near the boxing centres," Sailor insisted through his thick lips. "Can't travel a long way to a fight. I was too tired. I'll slaughter him next time though."

"Yes Jim? but...," Joe didn't know how to tell Sailor that he couldn't be his coach, or his sparring partner or even a professional himself. "I've got a girl friend who wants me to give it up." His imagination came to his rescue. "She's wanting me to partner her at tennis."

Joe was lying. His reality, like Sailor's, was failure. Failure with girls, with boxing, with horse riding and with tennis. He looked at Sailor Jim's battered face. "You ought to give it up mate. If the war starts again we can always volunteer ourselves to test for land mines. That won't be so bad as this. We might even have a few successes."

Joe helped Jim clean himself up. As they shuffled down the Knavesmire and on to Leeds Road, heading for York station, Jim poured out his anguish and disappointment into Joe's sympathetic ear.

Sailor fell fast asleep in a third class compartment on the nine-thirty Castlebrough train long before it was due to leave the station. Joe took the opportunity to pop up to the front.

He found his favourite engine, D49 number 2726, backing up. Jim Simpson and Alf South waved from the cab. "Now then Wadey, what yuh doin'."

"I fancied a bit of firin' tonight, this old girl's me favourite."

"Not blinkin' likely mate," yelled Alf defiantly as he dropped to the platform. "I've waited all year for a mainline job, an' I'm hanging on t' this, besides yuh not even on pay. What's yuh game?" Alf dropped between the stationary loco and the first carriage as Joe replied.

"Oh nothin' really, its 2726, she's just an old friend."

Alf heaved the coupling over the hook and then grasped the ends of the vacuum hoses, "Giv' over yuh softie, its ma turn, somebody'll only tek it off me over me dead body." Having finished the coupling task he squeezed back up between the buffers and onto the platform. "An' don't think yuh can sit on the fireman's seat either."

Joe slapped Alf across his shoulders, "You're alright, I'm travelling back on the cushions with Jim Packet. I was just checking to see who the crew were, wanted to be sure we'd get home alright."

"You alus were a cheeky young beggar." Jim Simpson called from his elevated position in the cab. "Yuh can be the cow-catcher tonight, if yuh need summat to do?"

"See you all at Castlebrough, I'll time the train, give you marks out o' ten for effort."

"Go on, get lost," Alf prodded the firing shovel in Joe's direction. "Or I'll have yuh."

The evening of the world heavyweight eliminator fight on April 15th 1947 seemed a long time coming. Weeks had passed, or so it had seemed, since the bets had been placed. Only Sailor Jim Packet had a seat at the ringside in Harringay. The others, who by now all felt rather foolish on their rash gambling, were nervously listening to the radio commentary. Some were at home but a small group had gathered in the Railway Tavern to listen on the Landlord's set in his back room.

Wade, Wagget and South were all more worried about their stakes than their Yorkshire Idol's hide as they pressed themselves closer to the set.

A tumultuous roar of cheers and applause crackled through the radio set's ageing loudspeaker as the former Yorkshire railwayman stepped into the ring.

"Where the 'ell yuh been wi' them beers," garbled Wagget, as Hibson finally appeared in the room clutching four pint pots. Hibbo's answer was lost as more noise spilled from the radio. The big Pennsylvanian miner had appeared in the ring.

"Baksi's a mighty man. He fills his corner, but he looks nervous." the commentator's excited voice gathered momentum. "Woodcock's bouncing on his toes ready, ready for action fit and relaxed. The referee's got them in the middle of the ring. He's telling them. A clean fight, the usual warnings. Pushing them back. There goes the bell. Woodcock's going for him."

"Come on Bruce get into him," shouted out Joe as excitement boiled over from the commentator. The locomotive cleaners with their fortune resting on Woodcock's skill were ready to take the punches with him. Fists flew amongst the growing band of listeners and comments flew thick and fast.

Wagget shouted, "Hush you lot, I can't bloody 'ear. Hibbo, let's hear it for Christ's sake." The volume was increased.

"Woodcock's going in, fast, skilful....., but wait, a right hook from Baksi rocks Woodcock. Woodcock scores with a straight left at Baksi's head but Bruce can't halt him. Baksi's driven Woodcock into a corner, Look! look at those left hooks, Oh if only you could see that uppercut to the chin, Woodcock taken a right cross from Baksi. He's down, what a disastrous start, Woodcock's down. Oh! oh! he's taking the count."

The seated band of locomen all clasped their heads. Hibson moved first. "Come on Bruce," he yelled banging his fist down hard and spilling some beer. Nobody cared about the beer. The noise from the radio was tumultuous then suddenly they went quiet as they hung on the count.

"Come on Bruce...., Yes, he's struggling up. The ref.'s holding Baksi back. The bell, the bell saves Woodcock on a count of nine. Oh boy! did he take it on the chin." The seconds ticked by, then into round two.

"C'mon Bruce, we're rootin' for yuh."

"Wow, good gracious Woodcock's down again, one, two, three, the counts going on, seven, eight, he's up, he's dazed, he's keeping out of trouble, nearly, a blow to the body, oh, and Woodcock's, down again."

"I can't take anymore." Joe groaned and grasped his drink for comfort.

"Jeez," exclaimed Hibson.

"Oh, God," cried Wagget. Their calls of despair spilled into the room, each was consumed by the commentary as it roared from the speaker like a runaway express. The suffering continued, it continued for Woodcock, it continued for the spectators, it continued for the listeners.

"If you could see Woodcock's face, swollen, bloodied. He wont give up, the Yorkshire boy from Doncaster is fighting back, but he's injured, Bruce is injured. The ref.'s going to do some..., he's finished it. He's finished it in the seventh, yes, in the seventh, none too soon. What a fight! What a fight? The courage of Woodcock. Baksi's the winner, he's going on to challenge Brown Bomber Joe Louis, Baksi could be the next World Heavyweight champion."

"Turn it off," Joe shouted out. "I can't take it."

"Shut up Wade, shut up you lot. What's 'e saying."

"A bad night for British Boxing. Woodcock's being taken to hospital. "What a courageous fight from Bruce Woodcock, a one time Doncaster railwayman and....."

The radio set went dead in response to Willie Wagget's ultimate censorship. The battered listeners in the Railway Tavern trailed miserably out into the peace of a cool evening. Joe's hankering for fame in the boxing ring was well and truly knocked out of him.

"What did you lads make on the big fight," asked Frobisher of Joe, Alf, Mason and Wagget as they arrived at midnight for night-shift cleaning duty. Only the shed fitter, Jack Fletcher, was present in the messroom along with Bill Frobisher who was writing out the following day's manning rosters.

"As I was saying, Jack when these lads came in, it wasn't a good night for our Bruce Woodcock. Bill Clarke was saying that the papers said Woodcock fought seven of the most wicked rounds ever endured by any fighter anywhere. I was real sorry to hear of his pounding."

"Not as sorry as I was," chipped in Wagget.

"Nor me. You got a fiver off me," complained Hibson, "You're not sorry about that are yuh? Come out o' the mess room Bill, there's an engine need's steaming. We'll set yuh alight and chuck yuh in the firebox."

Frobisher parried in like manner. "That's real nice of you, thanks, but, I knew Baksi would win." Frobisher brimmed over with self confidence. "How did I know? And I did know? Think about it, there's always somebody that knows, and I knew. I'll tell yuh how I knew and I'll give yuh all your fivers back."

They all stared at each other with disbelief written across their faces. Had Frobisher really offered to give them their money back? Hibson broke the stunned silence, he had never trusted old Frobisher. "Oh yeh, another clever trick then." The others didn't trust Frobisher either but chose to keep their thoughts to themselves, discretion might just be the better part this time.

Frobisher wasn't finished, "Yes I'll tell yuh, but, yes there's a but, a big but," he continued after a pause in which some whispered conversation took place. "You've got to swear that you don't tell anybody. Don't repeat anything I say to you. If you do let on, you'll have to give me the fiver back."

They queued up and collected their fivers off him. Each heard Frobisher's whispered remark and remained silent. Each fought to hide the startled expression that settled across their faces as Frobisher finished his hushed messages in turn.

With their fervour tamed, they all passively agreed to commence work cleaning B1 class locomotive 1010, named 'Gnu' which, very surprisingly was painted in the pre-wartime livery of the L.N.E.R. and stood on shed rather like a celebrity. They left the messroom with the superior Frobisher disinterested in them now they had submitted to his will. Frobisher really was more wily than the men gave him credit for. He knew of their little indiscretions at work; taking coal home, leaving early, using railway property for their own gain, even using engines to move private property about Castlebrough. He knew and he would always wait until he could blackmail his subordinates into submission. A smirk was apparent on Frobisher's face as he silently acknowledged that he'd bested them once again and he'd ruled the roost without anger or colourful expletives.

"By God," said Wagget, as he walked from the messroom. "That was close, that fiver was more than my week's wage. I'd 'ave been livin' in the dog house if our lass had found out. Hey ho," he added "it's off to work we go." Willy led the way to collect their primitive hand lamps, cotton waste and paraffin.

"Well I'm doing alright," said Joe, displaying two five pound notes. "Even though Woodcock had lost and I'd placed a fiver on him to win."

"How did yuh manage that then?" queried Hibbo.

Joe swore them to secrecy and then he told them of the fifty-six minute run to York and the five pound notes he and Bert Woodley had been given by the millionaire. "It was a surprise to hear him say that he was for nationalisation even though he was shareholder. He really is a millionaire, owns racehorses was a big firm of turf accountants in Leeds." said Joe confidently. "Posh office he'll have. I reckon."

"I've never met anybody who keeps account of turf?" South said blandly, though with just enough mischief in his voice for his colleagues to realise he was joking.

"Shut up tryin' t' be clever, Alf," said Wagget. "Or I'll turf you through that door."

"Careful, yuh'll strain that single brain cell you've got. Where is the fiver then?" Alf asked.

"Hey! look here. Two fivers," said Joe. "One's from moneybags an' t' other's my wages back from Frobisher. Oh and these two pound notes," Joe produced them from his back pocket. "Mack gave us them before we left for York. A tip, 'cause the train and it's loco were much cleaner, and the heating was on."

"That's for us then," snapped out Wagget. "We cleaned the old engine up for yuh, c'mon share it out."

"Drinks at least Joe?" appealed Mason."

"What about me?" tee total Alf made a plaintive cry.

"Alf? A quarter of jelly babies," grinned Joe in answer. "All girl jelly babies. That alright?"

"It's the pub then at twelve."

"After the goody shop," concluded Alf with a childish giggle.

The chatter subsided and, almost gleefully, the group of young Castlebrough steam railwaymen set about their prosaic task.

Six hours later, 'Gnu' eased out of the dark shed under her own steam. The weak silvery grey light of the spring daybreak reflected gently off her smooth paintwork and outlined the clean lines and curves of her her shape and form.

"We've done well there lads," whispered Alf to his mates, "Bloomin' 'ard and filthy work, but isn't she just a beauty."

As they rested and looked on, the early morning sun pierced the veil of thin cloud that had earlier accompanied the first hint of dawn. Its celestial rays shone through the drifting, whisping clouds of steam that cloaked 'Gnu' and momentarily bathed her in a divine aura of incandescence. Pride swelled in their hearts. She stood resplendent, a glorious testimony to their efforts.

A few hours later found the foursome together again in the bar of the Railway Tavern. Frobisher had told Wagget some interesting news.

"May the 10th, a Saturday," he repeated. "That's what the green B1's for. It's working the first train out of the new station at Filey Holiday Camp."

Joe got up and went to the bar, Wagget, temporarily putting his news aside, followed.

"Mine's a double Lambs Navy," the insistent Wagget pushed his way up to Joe whose hand displayed the two pounds that he had been forced by his friends to sacrifice on the altar of 'Bacchus'.

"I'll have a pint," Hibson called from his seat. "Oh, an' don't forget Alf's jelly babies."

"It's jelly babies or half pints, ain't it Joe?

"It's jelly babies or Adams wine," Joe declared as the two pounds were removed from his grasp by his best friend as they all jostled around the bar.

"Got any jelly babies, Norman?" Joe addressed the barman. "A quarter of all boy jelly babies please, Alf wants all boy one's, as he reckons there's more jelly on 'em." A chorus of laughter broke out aimed at belittling Alf.

"The thought of you daft buggers driving trains frightens me to death," the barman said, adding his unsolicited pennyworth of opinion. "I'm stopping with horses. They've more sense than you silly lot."

"Aye, yuh bloody right there, Norm," grunted Mowser, a dour brutish gas works employee and regular at the Tavern's domino table. His concentration had been broken by the mirth and his irritation showed.

The foursome assembled around a table and in a hushed whisper they continued their debate. Wagget produced the latest edition of the Castlebrough Evening News.

"Bruce Woodcock's going to be at Filey Holiday Camp."

"What's it say?" Joe craned his neck to see but Bill Wagget continued to read aloud.

"He's out of hospital. He had a broken jaw. Well he's coming to Filey for a number of weeks and Baksi, and his wife, are going to stay with him."

"Hey, if we could get into the camp and see 'em first hand, that would be good." Joe became excited about the prospect even though he'd given up any idea of boxing, pro or amateur, but that didn't matter now.

"Easy to get in, I know lots o' ways. Yuh just don't have to get caught by one of the door guards that's all. What's that say? Down at the bottom of the page." Hibson pointed and Joe read aloud.

"There will be many hundreds of guests at Butlins next Saturday for the official opening of the new station." Joe relayed the list of dignitaries which included local Mayors and Councillors, Members of Parliament and L.N.E.R. board members.

"What's the fuss about? asked Mason who'd just appeared on the scene.

"The official opening of the new railway station at Filey for the Butlins camp, there's going to be four platforms, long platforms." Wagget beat Joe in the struggle to do the most talking as loudly as he could.

Fortunately for Joe, Willie Wagget was the one who received the abusive verbal onslaught from the gas worker. "Can't yuh bloody keep yuh big mouth shut? I've just thrown that bloody game away cos o' yuh big open gob."

Wagget, presumably emboldened by his pint of Moors and Robson's made as if to rise and respond. A smile rather than a grimace clothed his face. Mowser stared intently at him.

Hibson's hand pulled on Willy's arm and he bent over to hear Hibson's advice. "The last bloke that spoke back t' Mowser like that went out through that window like Dan Dare. He didn't stop flying 'till he landed in Washbeck coal yard."

"That's over the road. An' they haven't found him yet," added Joe winking at Hibson.

"Okay, okay," Willy acknowledged Mowser with a salute, "We were just off." Willy turned for the door and the rest of the group gulped down their drinks and hastily followed his exit.

4
Big Wigs at Filey

Joe was eager to visit the camp and the new railway station on the Saturday of its opening. Alf, the less adventurous one, or, the more cautious of the two, depending on who's viewpoint was being expressed, was wary about Joe's plans.

"I've changed my spiv day." said Joe to Alf. "So I'm off work, free, to spiv about, I'm going to the camp" He left no doubt in Alf's mind. "Even if you don't come."

"Well OK." agreed Alf.

"Good on yuh," replied Joe. "We'll get on the first train going to Filey. If we wear our gear, we might just cadge a ride on the footplate, get the driver to drop us at the new junction cabin, then walk up the cess to the station." Joe stared at Alf awaiting a response.

Alf hesitated, "Let's get a free pass, it might just look more authoritative?"

"Okay, as long as you're coming." Joe conceded.

"We'll be down at the blood..., I mean, blooming dole office if we're not careful. You nearly made me swear then, you so and so."

"Never mind Alfie, lad, Grandad'll look after you," encouraged Joe.

"You'll be the next man, Joe, to be made up to fireman, I heard Frobisher saying," said Alf changing tack. "You won't want to throw that away by querying your pitch now. There's going to be a lot of big-wigs at Filey."

They clambered up from the new rails and ballast onto the newly constructed platform 4. There were no security personnel to question them. A little way down the platform a large crowd was assembled. "Dignitaries? What dignitaries are, I don't know!" stated Joe, "That's what the papers have been calling 'em though."

"There's Sid Jackson, Mayor of our place," said Alf.

"And other Mayors, of Bridlington, York and Hull, maybe other hobnobs too. Somebody mentioned a Lord Middleton, I think, the Lieutenant of the East Riding."

"Keep your lip buttoned, Joe. I heard there are directors of the L.N.E.R.

and Butlins' bosses." Alf sounded distinctly nervous. "We're here in our working togs. We'd a' been less conspicuous in our best clothes."

"These are me best clothes," said Joe, holding his chin up and dusting his overalls down. "Anyway, who's the bloke speaking? What's he on about?"

The man was Lord Middleton, he was referring to the forthcoming nationalisation of the railways at the end of the year. Much laughter rang out when the crowd heard him say, "I trust that this station will bring satisfactory results to the railway shareholder of today and, perhaps, the overburdened taxpayer of tomorrow."

"He's doing summat, Joe."

"He's pullin' that rag off the board, he's unveiling the station name board. 'Filey Holiday Camp'. What a lot o' fuss about a new station?"

"Four platforms and also sidings. Two island platforms he's saying, 900 feet long." Joe paused to listen, then said, "It's one of the biggest stations around here."

"Must be important, built to last a couple of hundred years."

The crowd started to turn after Lord Hamilton, who had opened the proceedings, announced that the first holidaymakers train from this new station was preparing to leave for York.

"Should've been t' Hull. that's biggest place in Yorkshire."

"Course it ain't," replied Joe.

"Course it is. Don't yuh know that."

Their dispute continued briefly until they arrived alongside the bright, clean one hundred and thirty ton B1 class locomotive resplendent in pre-war Apple Green livery and ready to take its rake of ten corridor bogie stock on to York and beyond.

"I'm going aboard," Alf said, "I cleaned the blooming thing, so I'm going aboard." he called out to the crew in the cab of the B1 loco.

'He'll soon get booted off,' Joe thought, then added audibly to Alf. "I'm going to see if there's any filming taking place, I might just see Woodcock and Baksi an' all." Alf was already in the cab of 'Gnu' before Joe had finished his sentence.

The crowd drifted noisily towards the main camp entrance, gaily decorated, welcoming and displaying details of events. The bill posters announced 'LONDON INTERNATIONAL ORCHESTRA, CONDUCTED BY FISTOULARI with SOLOIST SOLOMON performing for the three evenings over the weekend'. This highbrow advert surprised Joe. He was familiar with the jokes about wire fences keeping the holidaymakers confined, but 'cultural indoctrination' was a new prospect to Joe. He wandered up to the gateway, ready to respond to any request. After all, he was a little nervous about his visit which was unnofficial, almost sneaky.

"Passes please, show your passes. Your pass Sir," a Butlins attendent in red blazer and white trousers addressed Joe directly.

"L.N.E.R. pass," his thumb and forefinger held his rail ticket aloft with the word 'pass' carefully displayed to the attendant.

The face beneath the broad white trilby nodded. "Thank You Sir."

Joe gasped, he'd just recognised the attendant. The Butlins 'Redcoat' was Johnny Marsay, his fellow passed cleaner at the shed.

Joe started a question. "How.....," but an expressive wink from his shed mate underlined the validity of Johnny's presence. He waved Joe through the access gateway into the camp grounds.

The sight of the boating lake, the swimming pools, theatre, the roller rink, fairground and gardens hewn and crafted out of the coast shoreline soils appeared invitingly heaven-like to Joe. He'd never been on holiday, never had a family holiday, never mind a holiday in a man-made pleasure paradise like Butlins of Filey.

"Have you eaten yet driver?" asked a voice close by, it was another attendant, another of Butins' redcoats.

"No, I haven't, haven't really had the chance. I'm hungry though."

"That large tent, the marquee," pointed the redcoat. "That's where you want to be."

"But I've only got my L.N.E.R. pass, that won't allow me in there."

"Course it will. Here take a refreshments ticket."

"I'm not dressed for that."

"Go on Sir, there's a full dress meal for the directors, Mayors and top brass in the small dining room around that corner. You'll be okay to get something to eat in the Marquee. Joe Baksi, and Mrs Baksi, are about. Yuh might see them."

"I thought Bruce Woodcock was here."

"He is, but he's still keeping to his chalet, he's not well enough yet to be struggling with this crowd."

"I'd like to see him," said Joe enthusiastically.

"You might if you stand near his chalet. He came here last Thursday. There were a few campers here but they've gone home. The new crowd are just coming in. They won't know he's here yet."

"I know you from somewhere," Joe looked quizzically at the redcoat.

"You might, I was a railwayman once, from Bridlington shed. I worked as a fitter's mate."

"Yes, you looked at our big end, when it was getting hot, back in 1944."

"Aye, with Simmy of Castlebrough shed, you had a load of Brens. That's it. I remember you now. How you doing?"

They talked for awhile until the redcoat was summoned by a man in a pin stripe suit. "Best go and get some food now mate," the railway fitter turned redcoat thrust a lunch voucher into Joe's palm and he headed off in the direction of the Marquee.

Joe fed himself and listened intently. Close by was Joe Baksi and his manager, Joe overheard the conversation, about the punishment that Woodcock took. Baksi was quietly spoken, a large man with rippling shoulder and bicep muscles that called forth admiration from onlookers. He was a true sportsman though, he praised Woodcock's determination. "A British bulldog with all the courage and tenacity that we in the States have come to believe as being a part of your British character."

Joe meandered through the crowds. Almost as if it was meant to happen he suddenly found himself listening into another conversation.

"This red government, they'll nationalise everything if we're not careful, housing'll be next, you mark my words."

Joe's attention was drawn toward the voice. He stared at the face, so surprised was he that the sandwich he was about to bite into stopped short of his gaping mouth. It was the LNER shareholder again, the one who had made the official complaint over the Red Flag. Joe was riveted, so much so that his action, or sheer lack of it, drew attention to himself as if a locomotive headlamp was shining from his cap. The shareholder's head turned towards Joe and that expression of, 'Don't I know you from somewhere?' crept across his face. His lips quivered in anticipation of a statement, but an announcement over the loudspeaker put a stop to that.

"THIRTY MINUTES AND THE FIRST TRAIN TO LEAVE THE NEW STATION FOR YORK DEPARTS FROM NUMBER ONE PLATFORM." The stentorian tones of York's Lord Mayor's beadle bellowed the message clearly. Joe stuffed the whole sandwich in his mouth in one piece and turned sharply for the door with Alf's earlier comments singing loudly in his head.

Thirty minutes to go and Joe hadn't yet looked for Woodcock. He resolved to try and then return for his mate Alf South. Chance was on Joe's side now and he arrived at the chalet which housed Woodcock.

"When he's well he's going to train. His jaw was broken by a lucky one that Baksi dropped on him. Pity, that, Bruce could've had him. Big fellow, though, Baksi." A knowledgeable fan, who'd claimed his pitch right outside the chalet, kept up a commentary for the benefit of the ever changing and always curious passers-by and enthusiastic supporters. "He'll be goin' for his dinner now, so he'll come out this way. We've been asked not to trouble Bruce or make too much noise."

He's coming out now, he doesn't have to wait for second sitting. He's had some meals taken in."

"Course he gets special treatment, he's the special guest of Billy's."

"Of Billy? You know him? You do mean Billy Butlin, don't you?"

"Who else's called Billy?"

"They do say nobody called William or Billy get's taken on." The font of knowledge on all things to do with Woodcock kept informing the onlookers. They were rewarded for their wait and patience.

Bruce Woodcock shyly appeared at the door, probably because of his quiet disposition rather than feeling like a defeated fighter suffering some penance for not carrying his supporters to a shared victory. Gentle applause, contributed to with enthusiasm by Joe, accompanied Woodcock and his wife for a short way until a pugilistic looking companion quietly urged the onlookers to let the boxer pass unheeded.

A memorable reward for Joe, which was to become a popular boast was the hand offered by Bruce Woodcock which Joe grasped and shook warmly. Touched by hero worship and dictated by the urge to find his way from the camp to familiar territory he moved off wondering where Alf was to be found.

The crowd on number one platform had dispersed onto the train and occupied all the seats. The Apple Green B1 locomotive looked invitingly majestic at the head of the train. Joe was sorely tempted to take a look on board. The train seats were fully occupied. So popular was this first train out from the new station that even the corridors were packed with passengers.

The engine crew were ready for the off. "Hey Joe! a panting figure slightly behind Joe gasped out. It was Alf, Joe slowed and stopped.

"Alf! Are yuh coming on this?"

"Was, but it's full, not even standing room."

"If we don't get this well have to hitch back home." Joe thought their only chance would be to get on the footplate of the B1. "We've got rail passes from Castlebrough to York."

"Let's see if they'll let us ride with them."

"If there's no loco Inspector aboard we should manage it." Joe pressed forward with a show of confidence. "Aye Mate, have yuh got a minute?"

"Five minutes, to kick off."

Joe continued with the confidence that age and experience inspired. He hauled himself up the into of the cab of the tender locomotive. "You've got a real topper here."

"Don't she look beautiful. She just purrs along even wi' ten bogies on." Everywhere was sparkling, gleaming brasses, shimmering copper pipes, bright black paint work and a tidiness that was so pristine it cried out for attention. "Magnificent loco's these B1s, speedos, electric lights, rocker bars, hopper ash pans, self cleaning smokebox. A dream to drive, they'll have lasses firing and driving soon."

"Yuh still haven't got a privy."

"Aye, It's still a corner job that."

"What did yuh think of Oxford?" the question from the driver just seemed to drop from the blue then Joe knew.

"Of course, you're Harold, 'Yorky', they called you at Ruskin College last Easter. "You did the student speech on the Transport Bill. With your railway togs on I didn't recognise you? The train's packed to the gunnells. It's alright if we travel with you to York, is it? We've both got passes from Castlebrough to York and back.

"There's the whistle."

"Yeh," The fireman's reply started the journey. "Left 'and board in clear position mate."

"We're straight into the rising up-main, through Hunmanby. Uphill at one in fifty-eight to Speeton, over the peak and down to Flamborough."

Joe nodded.

"Of course you'll know this line well?" queried the driver of Joe.

"Yeh, me 'ome ground. Know every sleeper, crossing, and...."

"Even the lighthouse keeper at Flamborough," chipped in Alf. "And his daughter, an' all."

The even, clear exhaust-beat of the six coupled locomotive sent the rhythm of the accelerating train pulsing through their bodies. The slice of the fireman's shovel first invaded the coal-bunker, then swung to make the delivery of coal to its appointed place in the firebox.

Joe felt like a Lord. Here he was on a pristine loco hauling the first train from the new station. He'd been with boxing celebrities and had rubbed shoulders with influential people.

"Non-stop to York. Do you know the way we are going," Alf asked Joe. "Are we going to that place where the icicles were a foot thick?"

"Burdale tunnel, you mean. No. We're going over Speeton top, through Bridlington, then on to Driffield where we go off to Enthorpe. Up hill, a big one, then down to Market Weighton and Pocklington to York."

The locomotive devoured the miles. Joe's eyes soaked up the beauty of nature and the spring tidiness of the rolling Yorkshire Wolds. "We'll do a flanker then, as soon as he stops," Joe shouted to Alf. "I don't want to be seen on the footplate by a locomotive inspector."

"Do yuh reckon that'll be a problem?"

Joe answered as appropriately and as briefly as he was able. "Reckon we shouldn't be on the footplate without footplate passes."

Joe and Alf gave the fireman a break, they each took a turn at firing 'Gnu'. There was no struggle for steam or emergencies, signals were off all the way, treated it seemed, as a special train. "It might be special, workin' on double block regulations because of the special passengers," Alf paused in his firing duties to address Joe. "The Lord Mayor of York's on here. Did you see his stone o' gold round his neck. The Lord Mayor of Hull, Alderman Robinson, too. They were there with Billy Butlin." Alf continued his contribution. "I'm from Hull, mi home town."

"They only run double section protection for Royal trains I think," Harold returned to Joe's question.

"The dream train." yelled Alf happily to Joe. "I could make her steam on firebricks, she's so good."

"Up to Enthorpe now that we've passed through Driffield. Steep climb." Joe was displaying his knowledge of the road to the less experienced Alf. "Then down to Market Weighton. Forty-five mile restriction through the station." The journey continued without a hitch. Pocklington was passed with ease then on over the glorious viaduct at Stamford Bridge.

Elation brimmed over for Joe and Alf as they rolled into York. The green B1 loco and ten corridor coaches swept into the station and stopped on platform eight South, exactly where the station staff instructed by the exit barrier. The train carried the Mayoral party in one reserved coach at the front. The rest of the passengers, who were the first homeward bound holiday-makers out of the new station, occupied the rest of the train.

"Cheers Joe, see you again. Best clear off before the big wigs start crawling all over the platform."

"Thanks Harold its been a good day, See you again, maybe at Ruskin College on another trade union school."

"Yes mebbe, but get yourself elected on to the Sectional Council. That's where I'm going."

Joe was lowering himself down the cab side onto the platform. "That won't be easy for me, I'm an N.U.R man."

"Even they get on," laughed Harold who was obviously an A.S.L.E.F. member. Joe and Alf mingled into the crowd.

"Yuh there Joe?" the words sounded in the cab of the Castlebrough station pilot. A week had passed and Joe was on firing duty. He and his driver had just brought empty stock into platform one and were halted at the buffers awaiting the train's departure. Sailor Jim had appeared unexpectedly at the cab door. A shining bruise above his left eye and his thick swollen lips contrasted ridiculously with his smart suit, shirt and tie.

"Hi sailor, you look proper posh, where you going?"

"West Riding, I've got some digs sorted out. I'll get some proper fights in an' a new agent."

"Your off for good then? You didn't say."

"Yeh," Jim broke into a display of shadow boxing. "An' I'm not coming back to Castlebrough wi' out a pair of Golden Gloves." He slapped the side of the loco. "Not for me a life of shunting passenger stock."

'I won't see him again,' thought Joe, 'Hope he know's what he's doing.' Joe wanted to warn him off, to talk him out of it. The visions of Sailor Jim in the ring at York flashed through his mind, but Jim's brains were in his gloves. Instead of trying to deter him, Joe dropped to the platform and warmly grasped his hand.

"All aboard for Leeds," A guard's voice boomed down the platform. Jim slipped into the last carriage and hung from the open window.

"You'll make it, Sailor, I'll be at the ringside cheering you on. Hope your ship comes in mate."

A loco whistle interrupted their conversation and the train gently squeaked into motion.

"An your ship, Joe, even if its got eight wheels an' comes through Falsgrave tunnel." Sailor grinned widely revealing the gap where his two front teeth should be. As the train drew out his bruised face beamed like a tail lamp. In a last defiant gesture, Sailor punched his clenched fist into the air. Then he was gone, the last carriage slipped under the signal gantry and out of sight behind Falsgrave signal box.

It was the last time Joe ever saw Sailor Jim in Castlebrough or working on the railways, and the last time too that Joe ever thought of boxing as a career. 'Better a life shunting passenger stock,' he mused as he climbed back aboard the station pilot.

"C'mon Wade," grunted his driver. "Get yuh arse into motion, we've got the road, got t' shift the Hull stock into platform six."

1
Just the Ticket

The sea murmured soothingly and the gentle sound of the tide drifted up the slope of St Nicholas Cliff Gardens. It was a warm moonlit night, surprisingly for late September. Seated amongst the garden paths, on benches or in park shelters, were a few courting couples, talking or embracing, or watching the dappled moonlight dance on the rippling surface of the North Sea.

A distant shrill of a steam loco whistle accompanied by the metallic clanking of goods wagon buffers audibly intruded into the tranquil cliffside scene.

"That'll be the eight-thirty goods for York," said Joe plainly. Conversation wasn't developing naturally for this couple.

"Oh," said Rachael trying to stimulate Joe into conversation. 'He wasn't shy like this at the dance,' she thought. 'Maybe he wishes he hadn't asked me to come out with him.' Rachael was Joe's new girlfriend, they'd met at the Olympia ballroom the previous Saturday.

"Soon be Hull Fair. They're putting on two trains this year." Joe hated Hull Fair and yet he'd introduced the subject. Why had he mentioned it? He paused, trying to think of something more natural to say. "You said, last Saturday that you'd like to go."

"Yes, the lasses at Blowers are going. On Saturday night, they're planning a trip. They're collecting sixpences so that it's paid for. You know. Like a diddlum club."

"Are you going then?" asked Joe.

"I'm putting tanners in. I'm collecting for the packing department."

"So, you are going?" He wished she'd make up her mind. Why couldn't she be more definite. 'Answer the question,' he felt like saying. 'Carol,' he thought, 'always knew what she wanted. Yes, she damned well did. So it turned out, she preferred a soldier to me. But I reckon it was me, I messed her about, couldn't make me mind up.'

"Penny for your thoughts, Joe. Tell me?"

"Oh, I was just thinking."

'I wish he'd answer a question' thought Rachael, and then spoke. "I could tell you were just thinking. I just wondered if you'd take a penny for the thoughts."

"You don't want to listen to my stupid thoughts."

"Try me."

"Well," Joe mumbled. "Err, yes, I was thinking about those tides out there. That water near the pier might 'ave been washing up against the Himalayas this morning. Nobody knows do they?"

"I don't know." Rachael was struggling to understand Joe's profound, though somewhat irrelevant statement. "Have you been to the...., what's it, the Himalayas."

'Good God,' he thought. 'I don't know where they are, never mind knowing whether the seas wash up them,' he paused so long she thought he'd gone to sleep, then he said, "I was just speaking figuratively. You know metaphorically."

"No," she started off, being honest and then said. "Are you all right?"

They both turned, looked straight at each other and burst into laughter. The ice had broken a little.

"Tell me about your job Joe, if that's okay," she asked apologetically.

The ice melted with startling rapidity, although they had earlier agreed not to talk about boring old work, they now talked their heads off. The characters at their workplaces were discussed, they took on shape and became alive, their oddities and traits were described at length and laughed about. Conversation flowed freely, where earlier rigidity had threatened to stifle the budding friendship.

"Mister Blower comes creeping round the factory like a worried tailor's dummy, always saying, 'Come on Missy, stop talking, get on with your work'."

"I've never a seen tailor's dummy walking." Joe intervened, trying to be funny, but Rachael didn't give ground, or laugh at his humour, she just went on.

"When Blower called Nellie Cook, 'Missy' and she said, 'Don't call me that, I'm a Mrs,' he said, 'I know you aren't a Missy, Mrs Cook, your a Mrs, but I'll call you Missy because I've always called you Missy since you came here from school. That glue kettle's going to boil over Missy. You girls keep up the good work. I do Mr Jack Blower, Nellie says. She has a lot of cheek."

Joe responded to Rachael's chatter with the occasional nod.

"I heard her saying. to him, 'I earned one shilling and sixpence, piece work you call it, Slavery! that's what I call it.' She tells him off. Then there's Kathy, she's funny too," Rachael paused, reading Joe's expression. "You're not saying anything, What's up?"

"I was watching the moonlight on your hair, and glinting in your eyes." "You was what?" she laughed. "Sounds fancy, Rudolph Valentino stuff." "And your lips. I just feel the urge to plant a kiss on....."

"You just keep busy planting in your garden," she said gently pushing him back. "Plant spring onions or carrots, not kisses, kisses have habit of growing into families."

Joe laughed with her and tried to move closer again.

"I know railway firemen are supposed to start fires, are you trying to start one in me?" she laughed. "You're dafter than I thought you were last week, let's go it's nearly nine o'clock. We're talking nonsense aren't we? But I'm enjoying it."

"Let me give you fireman's lift up these steps."

"You can walk with me, Fireman Wade, but don't go looking for fires in my eyes, I'll think you're a bit potty."

Joe and his new auburn-haired girlfriend started climbing the cliff steps heading for home. Rachael broke softly into singing the popular tune, 'If you ever go across the sea to Ireland.'

"Hey wait on, I can't sing," protested Joe. "You'll have to teach me?"

"Hey Wade," Bill Clarke called out to Joe from inside the shed master's office. "Yuh've nowt to do, so just take this call-out ticket out to Simmy, in Nelson Street. D'yuh think yuh can stay awake long enough?"

"Sure Bill, an' I can be pleasant while I'm doing it," Joe said sarcastically as he dodged a badly aimed swipe from Bill Clarke.

Ticket-taking was a fought-after little perk by the duty engine cleaners on shed, especially if the delivery had to be made on evening shift. Usually, a delivery of a call-out ticket to an unsuspecting locoman for the following day's change of duty meant that the cleaner could go home early.

"I don't have a bike, Bill," lied Joe. "I'll have walk it, and then go straight home."

"Home? Of course, you mean the Tavern. You and Wagget are sleeping in the cellar, aren't yuh?"

The call-out ticket for Jim Simpson instructed him to work an extra train to Hull Fair on the following Saturday. Hull Fair was a glamourous, gaudy, and colourful week long spectacular full of promise and excitement for the visitors and an irritation for locals. It always resulted in extra trains.

"The bad beggar. Why didn't he tell me?" Joe muttered audibly to himself, annoyed with Bill Clarke's little trick. "What's he up to. There's two tickets here, one for Simmy, and one for me." Joe discovered that he was to be Simmy's fireman on the train for Hull Fair.

Rachael had finally asked him to go to Hull Fair on Blower's outing, but he'd declined. He'd thought he was rostered for the late cleaning shift on that Saturday, he told Rachael and she too had decided not to go. Now the call-out ticket informed him that he was going after all, as the fireman on one of the two trains from Castlebrough.

"The plans of mice and men gang oft' awry," he cried out to himself, recalling the well-known phrase from Robbie Burns' Ode to a Mouse. His bike rattled down Valley Road with his plaintive cries echoing uselessly across the cobbled street.

"You're on at the pictures from Sunday next week," Jim Simpson's first comment spilled eagerly forward as Joe handed the call-out ticket to him. "That film, Holiday Camp, is on, an' it shows 9881 pulling into Sandsend Station. Yuh were on that weren't yuh?"

"Yeah Jim, have you seen it?"

Jim's mind went to other concerns when he unfolded the call-out ticket. "Flipping 'eck, I could've done wi' out a trip to 'ull on a Saturday night."

"Me too."

With his ticket-taking duty completed he could assume himself free from duty at the shed. He cycled around the streets where Rachael lived hoping to find her by chance. His luck was in and he came across her linked arm in arm with two girl friends. He stopped to tell her news of his re-rostering for the coming Saturday.

"What a pity," Molly said, "Rachael would've loved you to come with us from Blowers. Wouldn't you Rachael?" Molly tugged on Rachael's arm soliciting a response.

"That trip's for the lasses at Blowers," said Rachael, possibly to avoid answering the question about Joe publicly.

Joe noticed that Rachael didn't answer the question directly and his heart sank a little. "I could still come with you, if you can get a ticket on the Blower's trip. I'll be on the engine but I can join you at the fairground on my break after I've left the engine at the shed."

"Yes, I could, there were still some places on Blower's party," Rachael expressed enthusiastically. "I'd love you to be at the fair with us."

"Good," responded Joe. "I'll see you on the platform at the station. Come up to the engine won't you, then we'll set a time to meet at the Fair." He spun his old Raleigh cycle around in a spectacular flourish of enthusiasm, shouted "Tah-ra, Tah-ra," and departed with a show of cycling speed, agility and skill that was totally unnecessary, but which might, or so he thought, impress the girls in some way.

The first week in October was the usual date on which the annual Hull Fair was held. Thousands of people and families travelled from all over Yorkshire and Lincolnshire to visit the event. Entertainments and excursions were enjoying a post-war boom. People were in the grip of post-war euphoria despite the shortages, rationing and other problems. But most working people now enjoyed a shorter working day, an annual holiday from work and at least a half-day off on a Saturday. New developments for most people and good justification for laughter, pleasant feelings and jollity.

The railway station at Castlebrough displayed two platforms full of colourful people awaiting their trains being propelled into the station from the sidings.

Two locomotives had been borrowed from York shed for the trains, one a recently reconditioned bright clean B1 locomotive and the other a rather dilapidated V2 class 'Green Arrow' displaying more than its expected share of rust. The V2 engine was allocated to Jim and Joe.

"We've drawn the short straw today haven't we?" said Jim as the engine backed onto the ten coach train in number three platform. "It's the biggest pile of scrap iron that's ever carried an engine number."

"You mean, a pile of old crap, Jim. Call a spade a spade, I say. Much more descriptive my way."

"Does anything work?"

"Only me Jim, that I know of, an' I'm not working very well."

"A V2 loco like this should be the best engine around here. The drop bars are not up fully, there's water leaking down the tube plate; smoke box door isn't air tight, sandboxes not full. Do you want me to go on?"

"No, but I will," offered Joe. "The front damper won't work. There's a blow in the superheater header, there's the leak on the brake pipe washer at the front. Fire hasn't been cleaned, the bars are covered with hard clinker."

"No good grumbling now son. We said we'd take her out, cos if we didn't the train would have had to be cancelled. Bridlington might have another engine. Just keep yuh fingers crossed and let's get going."

Joe couldn't see Rachael, or anyone connected with her. He stood high on the engine tender and scanned the crowd for her auburn hair. She wasn't to be seen. 'She's only five feet tall', he reminded himself. 'She ain't going to stand out in a crowd, not this crowd of giants on the move.'

"Joe!" Rachael's voice carried upwards to him on the loaded coal tender. "I'm down here," she cried.

Joe turned, a little startled at hearing her voice. He fed his eyes on her, thinking how beautifully arranged her hair was. He felt pleased and relieved to see her and jumped excitedly and somewhat carelessly from the tender into the cab. A loud metallic crack sounded as his heavy hobnailed boots struck hard on the engine fall plate, startling Jim who glowered indignantly at the sudden shock. Joe ducked out through the cab doorway and dropped down onto the platform. Rachael was with her friend Molly, but Joe had no eyes for Molly. Rachael looked lovely, a hint of lipstick added a dash of glamour and her hazel eyes burned with a welcome he'd not seen before. He felt an urge to embrace her, to say something poetic, to express his inner warmth and pleasure at her presence.

"Aren't you mucky Joe, How did you get in such a mess?"

He absorbed the metaphoric cold water without so much as a blink and smiled, "It's this coal in here." He then turned on the charm and whispered, "But you look lovely, beautiful and pretty......" But Simmy interrupted Joe's smooth patter.

"Hey Wadey, get up here, the board's off, and," he pointed to the two girls. "You two best get to your seats. There's the guard's whistle. They're closing the doors."

The semaphore signal controlling exit from the platform was in clear position. The girls ran back quickly to the first carriage with Joe watching to make sure they boarded safely. The guard's whistle sounded relentlessly. "We can go now Jim, there's the flag, board's off at Falsgrave cabin too."

Jim answered with a short pop on the engine whistle and steam surged into the cylinders An unintended lurch brought first the engine and then train into motion, shaking Joe and Jim in their boots.

"God, that was rough," said Jim almost apologetically. "I thought it was me, driving her badly. Did you feel that jerk, eh! Joe?"

"I think it's the tender draw bar coupling. There's slack on it. I moved her onto the pit outside the shed. The leading engine fitter was nearby and he said that there was a lot of slack on it, and that it needed jumping, whatever that is."

Jim let the conversation lapse temporarily whilst he paid attention to the track ahead and moved the train forward more quickly. The characteristic limping beat from the three cylinders of the V2 locomotive drummed in their ears. Despite its many shortcomings, the vibrant message of power gradually heightened as it accelerated.

Soon the train was speeding steadily along. They passed through Sander station where they had all clear signals down the junction line towards Filey, Bridlington, Beverley and ultimately Hull.

Jim attracted Joe's attention and waved him to cross the cab and join Jim on the drivers' side. A flash of excitement was kindled within him. 'He's going to let me have a little drive,' Joe thought as he moved across the rocking cab floor.

"Yuh were telling me, the fitter said the draw bar needs jumping, why didn't yuh mention it before we left?"

"I never really thought about it. I'm sorry I've never heard of jumping. I just knew that there was that slack, it gives a yukking sound if the engine moves off sharpish."

"I ought to have noticed it when we came up from the shed, but we were travelling tender-first, an' it didn't make the same noise when it was pushing the tender."

Joe was smarting a little at the reprimand, he should have told his mate, but it seemed such a funny thing to repeat. "I thought I was having my leg pulled actually," he said.

"Ha, well," Jim started on an explanation. "You know that the tender is coupled to the engine by a long bar of iron with a loop at each end. It can get stretched by the weight of trains and its got to be put back to its original length."

Joe nodded and listened with interest. "I do!" he exclaimed, "I've seen one outside of the fitter's shop, it looked so odd because it had two swellings at places along the length."

"Yes, they are shortened by the blacksmith getting a part red hot and then they jump it on one end until the swelling appears."

"Now I know," Joe paused and nodded with interest, then added. "I thought you were going to ask me to drive for a bit, when you waved me over at the junction."

"What!" Jim's expression showed total amazement. "D'yuh think I'd let yuh drive with half of Castlebrough on the train." he laughed emphatically. "Anyway, you aren't making her steam very well, look," he tapped the boiler gauge glass. "Keep the boiler full, we've got to face the bank up to Speeton."

Joe was familiar with the constant struggle for steam under adverse conditions that had been faced many times by every locomotive man. Jim Simpson and Joe Wade were no stranger to the struggle. They had extensive experience on which to call. They nursed and coaxed the steam pressure, keeping it well up as they climbed the steep bank from Hunmanby to the summit at Speeton.

"That's the hardest part over," shouted Joe as they began their descent into Bridlington "It's flat from now to Hull."

"Too early to tell. This job has a habit of coming up with surprises," returned Simpson.

The trip through Bridlington and on through the East Yorkshire village stations of Carnaby, Burton Agnes, Lowthorpe and Nafferton passed without further problem. Soon the junction with the Market Weighton line was reached where a signal check slowed their progress.

"Not too bad after all," Joe shouted across to Jim as they gently accelerated through the roofed Beverley Station. "We've been too pessimistic, Jim. I thought something would have gone wrong."

"We'll be there in ten minutes. In Paragon station," said Jim. "Then you can go and look out for your girl."

Crossing Walton Street level crossing was always an event that Joe enjoyed. Thousands of cyclists, or so it appeared, were always paused patiently on the road awaiting the opening of the crossing gates. No trainman looked out on the crowd without answering the cheery waves that train's passage seemed to inspire between train crews and waiting road travellers. Tonight there was the additional attraction of teeming life at the fair. The crowds at the gates were astounding. The ground shook as their train rumbled across the crossing, Joe cheekily gave a couple of whistle pops on the engine whistle without Jim's permission. Driver Simpson cast a censoring eye in Joe's direction.

"Sorry Jim, thought that dog was going to cross the line." How easy it was to tell a white lie.

Hull's Paragon Station roof covered a wide array of platforms and presented an impressive facade of long-span arches through which trains entered or departed. The track-bed and permanent way approach was extensive and it sported a myriad of semaphore signal boards. Through the complex of rails and signals, Jim Simpson carefully but hastily picked his path towards the station and the signalled destination of platform nine. The interior of the cavernous fifty-year old grand and imperial Paragon Railway Station echoed with a cacophony of railway sounds. Locomotive exhausts, clanging buffers, shunter's whistled signals and shouts, carriage doors slamming, all accompanied by a dense mass of smoke and steam drifting upward into the roof void.

The Hull Fair excursion had barely stopped at the platform before a man on shunting duties had their locomotive coupling and brake pipes detached. The shunter was so quick and Joe marvelled at his speed and dexterity. He handled all the heavy flexible pipes and couplings with a haste born of experience and strength. Joe descend from the cab footplate to signal a bell code to the signal cabin requesting exit for their engine via the adjacent shunting crossover.

"They don't mess about here. Especially when they've got extra traffic like today," Jim said as Joe climbed back aboard the locomotive which moved slowly over the shunting crossover towards the buffer stop.

"What mek's it happen like that?"

"Good local control and good men on the ground like that shunter who uncoupled us while yuh were still scratching yerself, an' they don't want people blowin' engine whistles out of place. Just watch it."

Fortunately there was a twinkle in Simmy's eyes but Joe knew he'd been mildly reprimanded. He had hoped to meet Rachael coming down the platform but their engine was released very quickly and in no time at all they journeyed tender-first to the sheds. No smoke, no blowing off of surplus steam and wide open eyes as they twisted and turned through the pointwork and around the bends to Botanic locomotive shed . Here they had to turn, water and prepare their poor quality locomotive for the later return journey home.

"Crike Jim! That was quick, my feet didn't touch the ground as we were liberated from number nine platform."

Their loco was quickly serviced and turned. "Can we go to the Fair on our rest break?"

"You can. We'll book off and walk up Spring Bank. I'll show you the way. I'll be calling on an old friend who lives around here, on the off chance that he's in. You go to the fair but don't get lost. I haven't forgotten about your escapades at Whitby t'other year."

The fair won Joe's interest. He had said to people that he didn't like fairs, they were a waste of money, but he was absorbed by it as he trailed between the sideshows, games and rides. Steam traction engines powered the multitude of mobile attractions and he soon found himself being seduced by the frivolity and excitement all around him. He hoped of course to find Rachael, but it seemed an impossible task amongst the multitudes of fairgoers.

A boxing booth caught his attention and drew him forward. Some tough talk was being broadcast by an eccentric looking, battered boxing character at the entrance door. "Easy money for you, or you," he said pointing to people in the crowd. "And you, that well built railway fireman over there. I'm talking to you," he emphasised, pointing at Joe. "C'mon big fellow, let's have some. Step inside, pay and watch, or fight and become rich. Easy money for you just a round with The Mauler or Sailor Slam. Come on and take the wind out of Slam's sails."

Joe shook his head, slightly embarrassed at the attention he was getting. The showman had a really well battered face. His nose was flat and his ears looked like cauliflowers, only red instead of white.

"Come on, up here Fireman," roared the showman. "There's easier ways of picking up a fiver than shovelling coal." Joe move towards the steps and applause broke out. He cupped his hand to his ear and asked for terms, shook his head, and stepped down again into the crowd to the accompaniment of comical boos and jeers.

"Get Sailor Slam into action," yelled the showman as an obviously half-drunk contender stepped forward and stripped for action. "Will Slam get slammed? This big chap's going to try. Two rounds for a fiver. He's just got to stay alive."

Joe gasped as the boxer appeared. "Wow! it's Jim Packet." Joe exclaimed audibly to himself. He was shocked, he recalled how he'd last seen Sailor leaving Castlebrough full of high hopes for a professional boxing career, but here he was working the fairground booths. Joe watched for a while as Sailor moved fast punching like a steam hammer until his opponent threw up his arms in instant surrender. At least this was a more skilled Sailor Jim Packet, not his old green pal of back-room sparring days.

Suddenly Joe had an ice cream thrust under his nose. He lurched back to see a crowd of Blowers' workers each clutching cheap and gaudy prizes they had obviously wrested from the stall-holders at great expense.

"Rachael." shouted Molly, but Rachael had spotted Joe. She grasped Joe's arm, even though it was dirty and smelled of coal dust, smoke and oil.

"You weren't going in there, were you?"

"Course not. Do you think I'm an idiot?" asked Joe, but it was Molly who answered.

"I was beginning to wonder."

Joe changed the subject, pointing to a big ornament Rachael was carrying. "That's a pretty little beasty, what is it?"

"I really don't know why I chose it."

"It's for her bottom drawer," Molly teased.

"It looks a bit like a pot dog to me." Joe offered that considered response after careful thought.

"He's very observant Rachael. A least he'll not feed you on pet food," chipped in Molly, Rachael's closest friend.

Joe now tagged along with the party of Blower's girls. But the hours of fun at the fair swept by. Joe's duty to the L.N.E.R. dictated his departure time. They left the fair and followed the sweep of the crowd along Spring Bank and towards the railway station. Joe left the girls and headed for the shed where he found his driver in the mess room drinking tea.

"We've still got the V2," he informed, "Control had a scout about but couldn't rustle anything else up."

"We'll have to make do then?" queried Joe.

The badly maintained V2 locomotive clanked out of the shed and backed up towards their waiting train. The two girls were waiting on the platform for the engine, Joe quietly invited them to inspect the foot plate of the giant steam locomotive.

"It's mucky on there. we ought not to go on in our best clothes."

In spite of their caution Joe persuaded them to squeeze carefully between the engine and tender into the cab of the loco.

"Which one's going to fire then?" asked Jim Simpson.

"It's big isn't it? Rachael replied questioningly. "What's all them wheels up there, they're too high to reach.?" Rachael asked.

"Joe, he'll tell you." answered Jim not really wanting to get involved.

Joe started on a pointed tour of observation of the controls but the clear voice of Nellie Cook carried into the cab above the noise of steam and fire.

"I'm coming up too. Move over."

Agony crept across Jim's face but fortune saved him from having to assert his authority and deny access to anymore unauthorised visitors. "There's the guard's whistle, come on ladies get into your carriage."

It was eleven o'clock when their train departed Hull station. The moment had arrived quickly for the last chapter of the evening to open. Soon after departure the train rattled past the still very active fairground and over Walton Street crossing thronged with late fairgoers at the gates.

Into the dark of the night and the countryside they plunged. Heads had been withdrawn into the train, windows were closed and revellers settled down to playing cards, singing, shouting or laughing.

Joe and Jim laboured within the confines of the cab of the bad-riding loco. They worked to keep a full head of steam, to keep an eye on every crossing, every station, every gate house and signal cabin.

Only the sudden scream of occasional passing trains invaded their cab as they powered northwards up the coast to Castlebrough. It was hard, skilled, almost scientific work for the fireman and the driver but they worked as a team; each sustaining the other, double-checking all operations. Joe knew the road as well as his driver did, each signal or other feature was observed by both and duly acknowledged.

The vacuum-operated train brake system had to be maintained with equal readings showing on the two gauge needles in the cab, that called for constant attention too.

"Be prepared!" Jim Simpson would stress. "You never know when something unexpected will happen. Be prepared for the unexpected."

"Driffield coming up Joe," Simmy shouted. "Look out for the outer home. I didn't see a light in the distant signal."

Joe crossed over the cab floor to answer, "I saw the distant signal, it was definitely off."

Jim spotted all his signals clear and opened the regulator steam ports in the boiler dome to feed more power to the engine pistons. The engine surged forward and yanking suddenly on the over-stretched tender drawbar, the whole train jerked and Joe was almost thrown from his feet by the sudden wrench. But just as he fought to regain his balance an explosion of steam, water and glass fragments blasted out just above his head. As the riveting sharp crack rung out Joe instinctively turned away as a hail of shattered glass struck him. Boiling hot steam and water sprayed out into the cab and for an instant there was chaos.

The cab was in almost total darkness, the firehole door was closed and the fire screen was down to shelter the driver's eyes from the glare. Joe reacted instantly with no communication to Jim who had the external safety of his train as his first consideration. Joe's overcoat was the first line of defence, held up momentarily, and then thrown over the bursting steam break.

The train was being brought to a carefully managed halt. "The right hand gauge glass has blown," Joe shouted out to Jim. "The ball valve hasn't cut in to seal the blow out."

Another coat, the inverted loco bucket and the firing shovel smothered the escaping steam further. Jim forced the top gauge valve shut and struck the bottom valve into closed position with the hammer. The rush of scalding steam desisted immediately. The rectangular glass shield around the gauge glass had saved them both from the full force of the blast.

"The ball valve didn't cut the bottom cock off," repeated Joe, "and a panel of safety glass is missing from the shield."

"You okay Joe?" Jim enquired. "Did yuh get any glass in your face, or scalded?" Joe acknowledged he had no injuries and asked the same of his driver.

"One gauge glass will have to do us." They checked with the train guard that all safety procedures had been observed and continued their journey. The engine whistle sounded and the regulator was opened slowly. Once again the rhythmical limping beat of the V2 sounded, but, there was a difference this time. A difference which both crew members immediately noticed.

Using his firing shovel, Joe clicked back the elliptical shaped firebox door on the ratchet, and heard the squeak of escaping steam. The wider the regulator was opened the louder the sizzle of escaping steam became.

"Yes, I know what that means," exclaimed Jim. "It's that blow on the superheater header, its blowing into the smokebox. That's what you thought you heard when we were still at Castlebrough."

"Agreed, but I've never heard a blow like that. Are we failed? Will we have to get somebody out to pull us in?"

"There's one train behind us, if we can get a clear through road to Castlebrough and get over Speeton summit, we'll 'ave done it."

They were hoping for a good run away from Bridlington but they had to stop to let four passengers off. "Bridlington coming up Joe, all boards off to Quay Crossing." Driver Simpson brought the train to a halt under the roof of Bridlington station and a few passengers disembarked.

"Here goes Joe," Simmy shouted as the first exhaust beats exploded into the night. "We've got the boards, do your best," The loco held it's feet on the rails and a brave strong effort was made to gain acceleration on the short level approach before the climb.

"There's no blast on the fire, Jim, what's wrong with the blast and the blower?"

"There won't be enough vacuum in the smokebox, that steam leak on the superheater will be the problem. There won't be enough vacuum to make the blast-pipe work efficiently and put a good pull on the fire." Jim said then turned all of his attention to external concerns leaving Joe to manage as best as he could.

Bridlington Station and Quay Crossing signal box shook as the V2 locomotive and ten coaches accelerated away at the maximum speed allowed. They whistled in answer to the 'whistle' board, and then struck out and up the long 1 in 92 incline to Flamborough and Speeton top.

There was no talking or shouting except where exchanges or instructions were necessary. The footplate cabin became a lonely place in the dark. With the driver's head out into the night, it was as if Joe was in charge within the confines of the cab. But the sway and roll of the locomotive, the yukking and juddering caused by the extended length of draw-bar and the physical intensity of the effort held no fears for Joe. Despite the problems he now faced he was beyond anxiety, he was as certain as possible that he would become Fireman Joe Wade before the end of the year.

The quality of the coal was bad, the fire-bed was clinkering, there was a multitude of mechanical problems but he coped laudably with them. But it became a battle in retreat, water and steam, the key elements, were slowly expended as the V2 drew its train labouriously up the incline.

"She's not steaming well at all Jim, there's no blast on the fire."

"Can you get that exhaust injector to work? It'll save you steam if you're able to use it."

"Nope, she's had it. We'll have to rename the ship Nelson."

Steam pressure fell inexorably and they were forced to submit and halt close by Bempton Station for a ten minute rally. To give up and call for banking assistance was unthinkable, that would mean failure on their part. They restarted again, still some way from the summit, and eased themselves slowly up the hill into the darkness. The incline levelled slowly and on what seemed like a last gasp the slope began to fall in their favour.

They'd made it, they'd climbed the bank, when the odds were stacked against them. They coasted down hill towards Hunmanby and Filey Stations and limped on steadily to Sander Junction and eventually a much relished arrival at Castlebrough Station.

"One hundred pounds of steam, and just enough water to keep the boiler damp," Joe yelled across the cab as they pulled into number two platform.

The crew hung on the side of the cab, tired but relieved, and watched the tired fairgoers shuffle slowly along the platform. A few happy exchanges and waves were made with the departing passengers.

"Don't forget to get washed Joe," joked Rachael as she and her party passed by. "You've got a bit of a black look."

"Not going 'round to your girlfriends then?" the train guard asked in jest. "It's only 2 am."

"Would if I could," replied Joe to the guard, then turning to Jim, commented, "We got home under our own steam. Didn't look like it at Bridlington. Did it?"

"Let's say it's been a fair experience, eh Joe?" Jim said with a little laugh, emphasising the word fair.

"Huh, not so fair when the water level was nearly out of sight." Joe slapped the side of the cab with the palm of his hand. "How does a locomotive get into the state like this one's in. It's only a few years old. Look at it, I bet York lent it to us just to get rid of it."

"Not just that, they'll hope we repair it, an' we'll have to, with all the problems, it's damn well unsuitable for traffic now. I'll be reportin' it unsuitable."

The guard added, "Aye, the whole railway industry's run down, there's been six years of war an' nowt after. Everything's worn out."

"Me an' all," said Jim, "Come on we've got the road for the shed."

2
The Longest Journey

"There's an excursion to Blackpool this Sunday, Clarkey said He doesn't know who can work it." Johnny Marsay was referring to the difficulty that the twelve hour rest period rule caused railway management. The rule was that footplate men must have twelve hours off duty before starting a fresh shift. "The Blackpool shift starts at nine am and isn't due to finish until four-fifteen the next day, Monday morning. There isn't anyone can do it and get in their proper rest."

"Well I'm not grabbing for it. I've had enough with long hours on the coal train." Joe thrust his shovel along the wagon floor, loaded it with coal and then threw it into one of the barrows standing alongside. "Don't much care for this bloody job either," he grumbled.

"I don't either," echoed Hibson. "Stacking five hundred ton of coal ready for the next coal shortage isn't my idea of being a fireman."

"That Blackpool job, I could get it Joe," said Johnny enthusiastically. "If yuh work my five pm bumming shift on Saturday night an' let me work your shift on the five am Gallows pilot."

"Not likely, pal, give up a Saturday night out and work on five pm bumming so that you can rake in a fat pay packet." It had been his intention to be firm and not to reverse his decision but quirk of fate was about to occur.

"Wade, there's a young lass to see yuh at the shed gate," an always abrasive Bill Clarke shouted across the yard. "Don't be long about it. The L.N.E.R. ain't payin' yuh for courting."

Without hesitation Joe dropped down from the coaling stage and hurried over to the shed gates. A short notice invitation had brought Rachael to the shed hoping to catch Joe.

"Can you get Saturday morning off work. I want to go and buy a dress for Molly's wedding. I want you to help me choose."

Joe would have preferred to say no, after all what did he know about dresses, but he was aware of a change taking place within him. He really liked being with Rachael, liked talking to her and exchanging letters on days when they didn't see each other. He was often to be found outside of Blower's factory waiting to meet her as she left work. His workmates knew of the blossoming friendship too and they wouldn't let him forget it.

"Yes, I expect so, I'll try and get it sorted this afternoon."

"Wade!" Clarke's voice boomed.

"I'd best get back, see you soon." Joe gave Rachael a polite kiss on the cheek and turned back into the shed.

"What's it feel like in yuh chest, kiddo." Arthur Wilko was stood in the messroom doorway. He'd just spotted Joe's kiss and was bent on making it into a joke. "Hey fellas," he called into the room. "C'mon see Errol Flynn." Wilko grabbed Joe's shoulder and yanked him involuntarily through the messroom door.

"C'mon then, What's it feel like in yuh chest."

"Why?" queried Joe, well guarded in case he was going to become the subject of a prank.

"Does it feel like you've got a ticklish feeling around yuh 'eart, one that yuh can't scratch."

"I suppose you'll know all about it."

"Well, that's love my boy, yuh's in love."

A communal guffaw broke out in the messroom and one of the old timers broke into song. "Daisy, Daisy, give me...."

The rest soon joined in. "Your answer do, I'm half crazy......"

Joe left the messroom hurriedly before any more coarse jokes emerged. There was nothing more that idle hands and minds in the messroom preferred than making cracks about workmates girl friends. 'Maybe this is love, I've never felt like this before,' he secretly admitted to himself. He arrived back at his job on the coaling stage only to find Johnny Marsay being helped down by Hibson. Marsay's ankle was badly swollen.

"He slipped over badly," said Hibson, "Looks like he's bust his ankle."

Marsay grimaced in pain as they both hauled him into the shed. "Won't get on that bloody Blackpool job now," he growled. Despite his obvious serious injury, Johnny Marsay could still only worry about his loss of earnings.

The following day Joe dropped in to see Dan, his wheelchair bound mate. They worked together making their own record player from a kit of parts that Dan had acquired.

"It's going to be the best that's available, with an electric pickup. No sound box." Dan exclaimed enthusiastically.

But Joe's thoughts were elsewhere. "I miss them bigger pay packets that we got in summer. I'm hoping to pick up a full pay-packet for the

Blackpool job, I'm expecting about ten pounds, just for one day's work."

Dan's thoughts were also elsewhere. "The chickens, Joe can you feed 'em. I can do this, but I can't get in to feed the chickens."

Joe didn't move. The chickens in question were six Rhode Island Reds being reared for Christmas in wire cages in a shed at the rear of the West's house. He thought that if he delayed feeding the now much bigger birds for long enough Dan's mother would do it for him. Joe had acquired the birds as day old chickens that had survived the accidental crushing of their livestock cardboard box when in rail transit. To save the six survivors from imminent slaughter he'd taken them home. Joe revived his chatter about his well-paid Blackpool journey due in two days. "I'll be with Bob Cass, on Sunday. We start at nine am and get back about four am Monday. Get paid right through. Double-time. I'll be as rich as the Aga Khan."

"But," Tom West intervened, turning from his Daily Mirror. "Yuh'll get booked off for seven hours if yuh arrive on time. It's a lodging job. If you're in Blackpool, booked off for seven hours you won't be paid. Yuh'll have to roam the streets for seven hours or more without pay."

Joe looked quizzically at Tom but the question that was forming was cut short when Dan spoke. "What about me chickens?"

Joe looked at the kit trying to divert the chicken issue, "Are you sure you know what you're doing? This gramophone'll be a pile o' broken junk?"

Dan was frustrated with his progress on the kit and his mood became aggravated. "Go and feed the chicken's pal, you know I can't get into that shed by myself. This wheelchair's too wide for me to get in."

Joe looked back at Tom, "What happens if we arrive late, Tom?"

Dan blurted out his chicken question again. "What about me bloody chickens, caw, caw," Dan squawked. "They want feeding. And I want to know whose goin' to pull their necks at Christmas."

"You are," said Joe. "I'm too squeamish."

"I'll be on me honeymoon. I won't want to be killing cock birds. You'll have to do it for me." Dan prattled on. "I can't kill them, they is all God's little children I say. Anyway there's me honeymoon."

"I've fed the chickens," Nancy appeared in the back room and interrupted the frivolous dialogue. "I've done it to stop you squawking."

"My dearly beloved has got the wedding breakfast ready for the hens and nobody looks after me," Dan exclaimed.

"What's this about a honeymoon then, you two getting married?" Joe expressed surprise. "You are joking aren't you?"

Nancy stood with her hands on her hips. "Haven't you said, Dan."

"No." Dan answered both questions at once and leaned closer to Joe. "I've just given way to tremendous pressure and surrendered myself and my estate." Dan turned his wheelchair. A pained expression conveyed Nancy's response to the chatter that persisted during her presence.

"I must be off my loaf marrying a lunatic like you, Dan, and such bad company you keep too. I'm going to have to think things over quite seriously I can see." Her face carried either a hint of humour or alternatively a mask of irritation, Joe wasn't too sure.

"That sounds promising," Dan blurted out. "She's thinking things over. Did you hear that Joe?" She passed by his chair and he let the carcass of the record player kit fall to floor. "There's romance in the air." he laughed, reached out and grabbed her raised arms and pulled her onto his knee. "Yes Joe, we're getting wed and I want you to be the best man."

"Sixteen shillings. That's very reasonable, all the way to Blackpool and back for sixteen shillings. Amazing what they can do with a railway system. Very reasonable indeed." Joe and Bob Cass listened intently to the passenger who stood by the steps of their locomotive.

"It's the men and machines we've got to get right. You've got good men on today, Sir. Good engine too," replied Driver Bob Cass with his characteristic short burst of accompanying laughter. "Are you interested in locomotives?"

"Yes. This one is an Atlantic, a C7 or Z class, if your an old North Eastern man. Good main line engines." He continued on to surprise Bob and Joe with the detail of knowledge he possessed about their particular locomotive. "I would dearly love to ride on one of these for a short way. I've never been on the footplate of a Z class."

"You'd like to ride on here would you? I'd like to let you." explained Driver Cass. "But you'll know, you'll need a footplate pass." Bob lifted his cloth cap to wipe his brow, he declined to wear a uniform cap. He continued, "On a train like this, and on a Sunday when it's not busy, I daren't."

"Yes I know. I know the rules?"

Bob was an easy chatterbox, making laughs if he could, being irritating if he couldn't.

"Perhaps I could come up at Blackpool, that's if it'll be all right."

"Aye if we get there." responded Bob.

"Oh, is there something wrong? With the engine?" the passenger sounded concerned, but Bob was really only joking.

"No, no," apologised Bob. "Its just my natural pessimism, my joke, I mean. Course we'll get there." He paused and looked over at Joe. "We will if Joe keeps steam up. He's been known to have leant on this shovel and gone fast asleep." Both Bob and the passenger had a little laugh at Joe's expense. Bob glanced at his pocket watch. "Soon be time to go. Best go and get your seat." No sooner had the words left Bob lips and the guard's whistle echoed down the platform.

"That's the flag," Joe informed.

Bob popped the engine whistle and as the signals dropped into clear position he opened the steam regulator. The train eased forward and the first exhaust beat loudly announced their start.

Joe started off in good heart. The weather was clear and dry, the rails provided a good grip for the four-coupled locomotive that strode forward firmly ejecting good clear blasts of exhaust into the sky.

The autumn leaves had begun their fall at the bidding of the changing season. Some fields had been ploughed for winter whilst others still carried maturing crops.

Joe laboured on the steady footplate, feeding the glowing heart with energy and expecting her to respond to coaxing like she was a living thing. He glanced upward at the trail of smoke and steam to check its colour and get an indication of the efficiency of his fire, approving of the hint of black smoke emerging from the chimney. He carefully shot three shovel-fulls of coal cleanly and accurately to the front end of the firebox and glanced quickly at the chimney head again noting the darkening of the exhaust just as he had expected.

They charged along and soon Joe had chance of a respite. He sat upon the fireman's seat and gazed casually out of the cab side. The train urged forward with the familiar clickety-clack of the rails beneath them, Joe's thoughts drifted.

"Dreams were made to be broken," shouted Driver Cass as he laid his hand on Joe's shoulder. "What yuh dreaming of?"

"Well, I'll just tell you, seeing you rudely interrupted my dream about her, I was just coaxing her along as fast as she'd let me."

"Pity Joe, I'd have helped you if I could."

"You could. I was dreaming about driving this old girl." He patted the regulator handle just in front of Bob. "This old girl."

"I knew that was your dream, that's why I shattered it for you," Bob chuckled away and then continued, "so that we could make it come true. Do you want to drive it?"

Joe was on the driver's seat almost before Bob had moved. He plucked his Grandfather's watch from his pocket and glanced at it. Then looked at the cut-off position, "On twenty per cent Bob. What do you think about me trying her on fifteen."

"You're the driver. What do you think?"

Joe did what he thought. He wound the valve up another five per cent looked at the steam chest gauge reading and opened the engine regulator fully. He watched as the steam chest reading rose almost to equal the pressure in the boiler.

Joe knew that he was doing sixty, maybe sixty-five miles per hour, on good straight, well maintained track, and he was on fifteen per cent cut-off.

"There's hardly enough blast at the chimney to pull on the fire," he shouted boastfully across the footplate to Bob."

"Give over talking. Keep yuh eyes open. Do what you think with the cut-off." Bob paused then leant over and whispered in his ear. "Are there any P.W. restrictions on the track? Did you look in the notice-case before we left the shed?"

Joe knew he'd been caught out, even though he was only the fireman he should have checked all notices before he'd left the shed with the engine. He stared blankly at his driver who licked his index finger and marked up two imaginary black marks on an imaginary black-board.

"We're okay, there aren't any today," Bob said with a suggestion of victory in his voice.

Joe soon got over that little embarrassment and felt as big as the Atlantic whose controls were in his hands. Bob was not watching him now, he attended to the firing duties, looked out regularly, maybe called out to Joe 'board off,' or 'distant at caution.'

The strong figure of a crossing keeper's wife could be seen at some distance with an arm raised. "See Mrs Smith at the crossing keeper's cottage, she's waving, thumb down to the ground. Yuh know what she wants?" asked Bob.

"Yes, a coal drop if we've got any. What would you do about it Jim?"

"I wouldn't drop any off at this speed, even if she was the Angel Gabriel. It'd bounce straight through the carriage windows."

They ran on smoothly, the steady discharge of exhaust steam at the chimney head a good indication of the ease with which the locomotive handled the load. 'So easy', Joe thought, 'Damn good engine, not a knock on any big-end or crosshead, or a flat spot on any wheel. She's running like a sewing machine.'

The day looked good, full of promise, the autumn greens contrasted pleasantly with the golden browns appearing on trees and the burnt yellows of the resting fields. The track bed was neat, weeded and orderly, station buildings displayed fresh coats of paint, some clear evidence of new standards and pride beginning to emerge after the neglect caused by the wartime experience.

Joe relished his responsibility as the driver and blew the engine whistle with a special emphasis and pride at the points where a whistle warning was necessary.

"Watch your speed Joe going through Rillington Junction, lots of check rails, shunts and crossovers." Joe heeded his warning and stayed at the controls.

Eventually Bob moved over and took control with the remark, "I'll take her on through Malton and on to York. Yuh never know who's watching. After York we've no stops until Crossgates and then Leeds."

"Thanks for that drive Bob, first time for me on the mainline with a passenger express. Fill up for water at Leeds do we?"

"Yes, but we'll also pick up from the water trough further on towards Lancashire. That'll take us on to Blackpool."

"Do you know the road Bob?."

"Only as far as Leeds, then we get a pilotman on board. I'll drive under his supervision. I'm still in charge of the train, 'till I've seen him look after me and the train. If he's good I'll hand over to him and let him drive."

Joe returned to his firing duties, they crossed the River Ouse and passed through York station in good time. On to Church Fenton and the hard, noisy pull up the rising gradient to Micklefield Junction. The short stop at Crossgates was followed by a gentle coast downhill and into the covered environs of Leeds City Station.

"Blackpool twenty-three are you matey?" intruded a voice at the cab entrance as the train settled to a smooth halt. "You're train number board's blacked up. Looks more like twenty-eight."

Bob Cass cringed at the matey address. He'd slept within close proximity of a Lancashire regiment P.O.W. in a prison camp during the war. The

Lancashire prisoner's incessant use of the word had irritated Bob with maximum abrasiveness. He looked across his engine cab towards the origin of the voice, almost expecting to see the sparse face of Sandy 'Sandstone', the one time British Army soldier who was always rubbing people up the wrong way.

"God almighty." gasped Bob, it was Sandstone. The laugh that usually followed Driver Cass's light hearted backchat was absent. He gaped out of the cab window at the slight, informally dressed, oil caked figure addressing him as matey. "Where the 'ell have you crept from?" There was instantaneous mutual recognition.

"Same place as you, matey, Jerry camps."

Bob's warmth and humour returned. "Yuh ain't had a wash since then, have yuh Sandy. Good to see yuh again, matey," he added the word matey with a special emphasis.

"I asked you a question, Yorkshire Tyke. Do you bloody well know your train number?"

"Still as bloody awkward as ever aren't yuh," answered Bob. "Twenty-three, isn't it Joe?" Joe nodded. "This is my batman, Joe, Not bloody comic batman, me own matey, puts coal on."

The verbal jousting was suspended while genuine warm handshakes occupied a few seconds. Joe climbed up onto the tender and put the water crane hose into the tender filler hole.

"Turn her on mate." he instructed. Bob turned the water on and returned to his conversation with Sandy.

"Blackpool, yes, that's us, are yuh going to be our pilot?" asked Bob. "For me sins."

"But, d'yuh know the way, Sandy? Yuh couldn't find the door in number ten hut when we were wi' the Jerries."

"I don't know where Blackpool is, on a map like, if that's what you mean."

Bob bounced back with, "Have they taught yuh to drive big engines yet?"

"No, they frighten me to death," stated Sandy mischievously. "You'll have to show me."

Joe shouted down from his position on the engine tender where he was still holding the water crane hose, "She's nearly full." Bob turned the water off. The train signals were in clear position and the guard was closing doors on the extra passengers who'd joined hoping to spend a few hours on Blackpool's Golden Mile or in the Tower imbibing the local brews. They were ready, the steam regulator was in the hands of Bob Cass when the guard's whistle shrieked out clearly above the background clatter in the station.

"I'll drive her for you Bob. It'll be easier for you. I know this line like the back o' me hand, I'll take 'er as far as Skipton then you have a go. The road's simpler after that."

"You've worked on C7s then, Sandy?"

"On everything Bob, drove Mallard for three weeks. I get around a lot of sheds. Garratts too, I'm not married so I get about a bit and I'll go for a loco inspector's job one day. Railways is me life now Bob."

"Take her over Sandy." said Bob, I'll look out, or have a spell with the shovel, give Joe a rest"

Bob had been many times to Blackpool and many times to nearby Morecambe but each time he was aided by Pilotman. The distance coast-to-coast across the Pennines was so great that a driver who knew all the road was not often available.

"Which way are we goin', does tha' know?" Bob asked.

"I'll tell you when we gets there." replied Sandy.

Once away from the urban sprawl of the West Riding of Yorkshire, their journey through spectacular Pennine countryside heightened their spirits. The beauty of the higher land coated in colourful autumn yellows and golds was captivating. They rolled on, steaming well and on time. The opportunity to pick up some water from the troughs while travelling fast appealed to Joe. He was given his instructions as they all viewed their approach to the water troughs. The long, narrow, troughs could be seen clearly ahead by all the crew, appearing much like a long shiny strip of mirror between the rails.

Bob explained. "Get hold of the water chute handle when you're passing the notice that says, 'Lower water scoop now'. Do it as fast as yuh can, then count ten seconds and wind the scoop up quickly. Yuh got that Joe?"

"Yeah, I've done it before."

"Tek advice matey," Sandy added his four-pennorth worth. "Get it wound up quickly, before the scoop hits the end of the trough. Get it up or you'll smash it."

"Yes, matey," Joe acknowledged.

"Now matey, down, DOWN, DOWN, whistle, count ten seconds......, up, UP, UP."

Joe's arm spun as he wound the water chute up. He had been soaked by the heavy spray that had shot upwards and outwards as they collected several hundred gallons of water at sixty miles per hour.

"Well done there, matey," chipped in the pilotman.

The loco pitched and rolled as it sped along at high speed but was a good workhorse. It speedily ate up the miles and eventually they crossed into Lancashire. "Red rose country now, watch yuh back Joe, an' yuh wallet." Bob said loud enough for Sandy to hear who responded with a grimace and a two fingered salute.

A few signal checks around Blackburn and Preston stations put them well behind schedule and they ran into Blackpool North station over three-quarters of an hour late.

"We've lost a bit of time. We're nearly an hour late an' we'll have to book through. We'll be here for less than seven hours, that means we can't be booked off." Sandy sounded jubilant. "Sign off and rest, sign on for allowances, but not for a lodging billet. We'll be paid right through."

The crew expressed joy at the announcement. Bob paid full attention to bringing his train to a close and steady halt in one of the long platforms. Doors opened and a torrent of working people flooded out eager for their hedonistic experience in Blackpool.

The crew had to coal, oil and water their engine and clean the fire out. This was a time when Joe welcomed modern mechanical aids like the rocker fire bars. Shortly they signed off for their rest period and found themselves strolling down Blackpool seafront.

"We'll tek yuh down the Golden Mile Joe," Bob said. "Yuh might mek it wi' some lass," he added with his usual punctuating chuckle.

"That'll be difficult, he ain't got 'is best suit on exactly." Sandy stated the obvious to Bob then turned to Joe. "You look like you've just come up from the pit and ain't had a wash for a week. That's what causes them spots, kid. Ain't that right Matey?"

"I reckon so, matey," Bob said obligingly. "I reckon those krauts, must 'ave taught yuh to call everybody matey."

"No, at one camp I was prisoner in, I taught them. I told the Jerries that to call an Englishman matey was an insult. Like calling him a load of crap and saying that his father was a monkey. All the Jerries took it up and before long they were calling us all matey. Best of it was all the prisoners were in on it and the joke was on the Jerries."

Joe laughed at Sandy's tall story but reckoned it was probably true.

Bob scowled, "When you get to be a loco inspector, please keep off my engine, matey. Look, you've got me saying it now.

They walked a little further on. Bob's thinning hair was covered by a neat blue, soft flat cap. It contrasted tastelessly with his yellow tie of some vintage. Though he looked a neat dresser stood next to the coal-dust stained Joe and the oil caked Sandy.

"Just look at the state of yuh two, an' I've got to walk wi' yuh both."

"You'll be after a bird then, Sergeant Cass? Done up in you glad rags, like that." Sandy ran Bob's tie between his fingers.

"That's the idea," chuckled Bob. "If I look like getting on wi' one, you two don't know me, okay?"

The Golden Mile was a glittering promenade, full of life, laughter and excitement. Thousands of cheap, sparkling bargain goods and seaside souvenirs dangled in every shop window. Ornamental lighting lit up the promenade which was jammed with cars. Decorated tram cars rattled to and fro.

"Blackpool Tower and some other places'll be out of bounds to yuh." Bob instructed Joe.

"Why?"

"Because, I'm the Skipper," he said puffing his chest out. "And because they wouldn't let you in the Tower Ballroom dressed like a coal-heaver."

"I'm not expecting to go dancing, but we ought to have a bit of a laugh anyway."

"You're not on your holidays Joseph. We're supposed to be on our rest period." There was a slight hint of feigned reprimand in Bob's voice. "We've got a long haul home yet."

"He's right matey," Sandy added more seriously to Bob's remarks. "We're all on pay, it's our rest period. You'll want all your energy for the trip back. I've seen men get drunk, lose their way in a strange town an' leave their train an' all the passengers stranded for hours."

"Who'll have some fish and chips with me?" Joe questioned, moving the conversation back to less serious matters. "Will you Bob, on me. Then I'll buy a newspaper and go back. Get some rest in readiness for the trip back."

Joe and Bob joined a queue in a nearby fish shop whilst Sandy went off alone to find a public lavatory. Bob had learnt more about his old, snoring, fellow P.O.W in the last few hours together on the C7's footplate than he'd ever learnt about him in the confines of P.O.W. camp. "He knew that engine, handled it beautifully, Not a bit rough. Good engine man! Didn't yuh think so Joe?" Bob didn't wait for an answer. "I always think yuh can tell a driver's train control from the way he takes his train into a platform. He stopped on a sixpence, so smooth a cup o' tea wouldn't have slopped over."

Sandy rejoined them and all three wandered slowly back to Blackpool sheds eating their fish and chip suppers. They found a quiet corner in the loco-shed mess room and rested for the journey back. Sandy and Bob gave their bodies over to relaxation and fell asleep, snoring away, whilst Joe took advantage of the rest break and got out his reading material.

Their ten-thirty departure into the clarity of the cold October night went smoothly with the pilot man at the controls. Bob spent his time looking out and watching for signals and would call out to Sandy appropriately. Joe was happy to do all of the firing, the quality of coal obtained at Blackpool was his only concern. It was very poor. 'Mushy coal dust' was the description he'd given to Bob. "When it lands on the firebed, it settles and cakes," he'd reported. It would slowly be consumed by the fire. The worry was that the mush would fall in a pile and dampen the fire. Its use called for all of Joe's skill, with great care he used the fire irons from the tender top to rake the fire.

As he manhandled the long irons he was thankful that there was no fourth man in the cab. Lifting the irons down from the tender top reminded him of Alf South's recent embarrassing experience with a red hot fire iron he'd been using. As he'd moved the hot iron close by the seated engine driver, the loco had bucked causing Alf to stumble. The iron had landed on the broken upholstery of the driver's seat and ignited it. The seat began to burn ferociously, but unnoticed by his driver. Poor Alf panicked, he threw the hot iron onto the tender top. Just as the driver became aware of the burning and noticed a growing heat, Alf threw the dirty water contents of the engine fire bucket over him.

The rest of the dialogue related by Driver Hustle to the shed master, and told enthusiastically in the messroom, had not been for delicate ears. Only a complete new uniform and a promise to keep Alf South well away from the him in future, was the only thing that placated Driver Hustle. He also insisted that a locomotive inspector travel on the footplate with the erring Alfred to ensure that he was capable of being a relief fireman.

"Sorry about reporting you son," Driver Hustle had grunted an apology to Alfred some time later. But his mates in the messroom never did let him forget about the incident. These humorous thoughts occupied Joe as he worked around the firebox with the long pricker. He very carefully replaced it back on the tender top when he'd finished.

Towns, tunnels, bridges and many other trains passed by in the night. The water troughs were used again. The poor coal troubled Joe a little but after a while a tired monotony affected him and his steam pressure fell back occasionally as a result of his enveloping lethargy.

"Leeds City in thirty minutes," shouted Sandy to Bob then you are on your own again."

"Water?" Bob shouted questioningly to Sandy. "D'yuh think we'll have enough water for the rest of the journey."

Sandy obliged with an answer born of experience. "Never assume you've filled the tank at the troughs. Fill up as soon as possible when you see a water crane." On arrival in Leeds station he stopped the train exactly in the correct position to place the wide leather hose of the water crane into the tender tank.

From his position on the tender top Joe heard Bob and Sandy say goodbye like old friends. Perhaps Bob hadn't minded being reminded of Sandy's matey expression after all.

The way home was uncomplicated by anything other than the poor quality coal. Joe kept his engine going, Bob helped by running easier, by giving Joe short steam rallies. The road to Castlebrough was clear before them. The night was calm and clear, signal lights sparkled and few words were needed to be exchanged between the crew on the footplate. Bob's cloth-capped head remained out in the night, to return only to glance occasionally at the water level gauges and to keep a wary eye on Joe's responsibilities. Long hours at work and the long journey were now tiring the crew.

They flew on into the night without a signal against them. York, with its tangle of permanent way and the legion of signal lights, slowed them but did not halt their progress. The mainline was clear, straight through York station, checked only by the speed restriction.

"Don't go to sleep yet Joe," said Bob, when he observed Joe take a gaping yawn "Forty-two miles yet before we get to Castlebrough and bed."

"Yes, I'm okay?" replied Joe. Slowly the forty-two miles slipped by as the tiring struggle to maintain steam pressure was sustained.

"There's the mast lights on the wireless station above Castlebrough, not far now," Bob called out.

"And the light on the top of Oliver's Mount War Memorial," Joe pointed it out.

Oliver's Mount, the steadfast peak dominating Castlebrough, had witnessed much through history. The Romans, the Norman Conquerors, Cromwell's rebellion and victory in the English Civil War. The adjacent valley had yielded for the turnpike road and the railway, blitz bombers, sea bombardments and much more. Tonight it witnessed Joe and Bob creeping in with their train towards Castlebrough Station. Red, green and amber flickering signal lights positioned against a clear sky in fixed patterns indicated their path into number three platform.

The C7 locomotive, shattered the early morning quiet with the blast of its exhaust as Bob propelled his now empty train into Gas Up Sidings. Signs of life were few as the locomotive rattled and clanked into the shed yard.

"You get yourself off to kip, lad," Bob instructed. "I've a report card to make out and the time sheet to finish."

Joe yawned and stretched, "So long Bob, see you at five tonight, we're both on the dusthole as we expected. No change."

"Aye, so long, don't yuh do anything that I wouldn't do," Bob chuckled in response and added. "Don't yuh sleep in, remember, five o'clock tonight on the dot."

Joe pondered sleepily as he wandered home down Sander Road in the darkness. His tired thoughts enveloped him, until he walked straight into an unlit gas-lamp standard. The bump shattered his private world and left him to suffer a red graze and a developing lump on his forehead.

It was nearly four-thirty when his key turned in the door and, obligingly, his mother who had been listening for his homecoming, came downstairs in her night clothes. He washed quickly and she tended to the newly grazed lump on his head, greased it with butter, and made a bacon sandwich for him to eat in bed. With the quiet of the night settling back upon the household, his Mother took to her bed again without complaint.

Joe ate his sandwich and reflected on the day of his longest journey. His tired eyelids drooped as he thought of his mother's patient attention so late in the night. 'Mothers are good to have,' he confessed privately, then sleep overwhelmed him.

3

A Spin on the Turntable

The Banns had been read on three consecutive Sundays in Saint James' Church, Sander Road. The names and intent of one Daniel West and one Nancy Danby had been read aloud in church without anybody registering a protest or a response.

Dan West's last night out as a bachelor was in process of fulfilment. The bachelors were only two in number, Dan and Joe, the event had been a spontaneous arrangement and no other bachelors had been invited. It was to be different from the usual pattern, they had agreed on that, but it hadn't gone further than two pints and it was threatening to be dreadfully flat, like the awful beer. Dan held his pint glass up to the light. "It's like gnat's pee this ale, I wouldn't give it to my worst enemy. Let's sup up, best not waste the horrible stuff now we've paid for it. We'll go somewhere else."

"You mean we will if the landlord doesn't see us coming. You try singing again like last week in the Blue Bell an' we'll never get in."

"We'll try the Railway Tavern then," replied Dan loud enough for all to hear including the Landlord.

Joe returned the empty glasses to the bar. "Thanks pal," grunted the Landlord who'd heard all of Dan's comments. "Best go before we chucks yuh out." The heavyweight Landlord stamped a foot and shooed them on their way. "Come anytime lads. Have night to remember."

Joe wheeled Dan off at reckless speed down Sander Road in the direction of the Railway Tavern where their arrival at the door coincided with the simultaneous arrival of Willy Wagget and Rob Hibson. Dan and his wheelchair were manhandled quickly and roughly up the steps and into the dimly lit interior of the public house.

The drink flowed more freely now as did the conversation. Alf proclaimed, "Let's drink to the magnificent musically unique band of the horological horse guards parading with their gleaming chronometers."

"Does that mek sense pal, yuh either a genius or a bloody fool, and I don't think you're a genius."

"Another drink Dan, its yuh last night of freedom."

"It's alight for you lot, but my Mrsssss, er sssorry," Dan slurred. "SSSShe isn't my Mrs 'till tomorrow, but she'll be waiting with the hammer and tongs."

"This being your last night of freedom," stirred Hibson, "what about coming down to the shed, we could join some of the lads, tek 'em a drink, get a game of cards."

The idea, although ridiculous and probably in contravention of regulations was seized upon by all. Bottles of best Moors and Robson's ale were piled high onto Dan's lap and the foursome took off down Sander Road.

The wheelchair brigade, now more than just tipsy, noisily presented 'Les Miserable in Marriage', a piece of impromptu audible and verbal rubbish they'd concocted themselves. This was followed by a murdering of 'On Ilkley Moor Bah't Hat', that left the Yorkshire song without hope that it might be ever heard in public again.

"Shut up, down there, you noisy louts." The instruction carrying the weight of personal anger fell onto them from a second storey gable window.

"Slush, Slush," Dan slurred in response to the complaint. "We'll wake all the other animalsssh. How much have you had to drink, Joe? You could get copped being drunk in chargsssh of a wheelchair on the public highway."

There was a pedestrian way into the shed from the back. A personnel door access had been made through the rear wall into what had been a fitters store. The wheelchair and its occupant presented no great problem to the combined strength of Hibson and Wagget.

"Don't get the wheelsssh in any oil or muck," Dan instructed as they carried him and the wheelchair into the messroom.

"The cards is out." Hibson said to four seated workmates in the messroom. He nodded in the direction of the approaching Dan, Joe and Willy. Dan's wheels scraped noisily on the sand strewn concrete floor as he was shunted to a halt. Bottled beer was freely handed out to grunts of 'thanks' and 'cheers'.

"Here's Desperate Dan and his pardner, without shooting irons and loaded wi' the paper stuff."

"Have a quick shuffle Dan," invited Wagget. "Go on Just one."

"One cut for a pound each in the kitty, that's all."

Dan suddenly seemed to sober up. "I'll cut, one hand, just to show you how good I am. I'm dealing. You cut, and you. Cut the cards, and again. A pound in the pot each of you. Red Aces high and another cut if there's a tie." He served one card each, face down. "There's yours," Dan turned a 'Jack of Hearts' over for Joe, then two lesser cards for Willy and Hibson.

Dan's own Ace of Hearts, stopped all discussion and interest in card playing. "Four pounds I win."

"Oh, how did you do that?" asked Hibson.

"No card games tonight I'm tired."

"I'm out too," chorused the quickly defeated trio.

"I'll do it again, another pound each, eh?" asked Dan.

"The three pounds, It's a wedding present from us three. We were kind an' we let yuh win."

"Dan the cards, eh," One of the duty cleaners spoke. "Where did yuh get that sensitive shuffle technique."

"Boy," Dan addressed them somewhat pompously, exhibiting a mock superiority. "I'm a watchsshmaker, I need ssshoft ssshensitive fingersssh for the job." He began slurring again. "Don't ever play me at cardsssh, I've just done three yearsssh in hoshpitalsssh and at college with the best playerssh and trickssshterssh in the British armed forsshessh. I fiddled yuh, yuh knew I could. Thanks for the gift of three pounds."

Frobisher appeared unannounced in the messroom. "What the 'ells goin' on in here. What yuh lot doing 'ere yuh not on duty?"

"It'sssh me night out, 'an I'm a guesssht of these lads." Dan held a bottle up and Frobisher took it, he became uncharacteristically charitable.

"Oh, all right Dan," then he changed the subject to something that was of concern to him. "Where's your Dad been recently, is he ill? He's been absent from work."

"No, he'sssh okay, on union businesssh. But he'sssh off work tomorrow for my wedding."

Frobisher's rude disposition returned, "You two," he grimaced at two duty cleaners. "Get out and start on that B1 in number two road. You've done nothing since you came on at ten o'clock."

Frobisher's allegation of idleness on their part was denied vigorously, giving the impression that the two duty cleaners were unjustifiably being harshly judged. When their protestations weakened Bill Frobisher issued new orders.

"Wagget and Wade, and you Hibson. Take Dan for a look around."

"Why?"

"Because I said so. Dan's never been in the shed, even though his dad runs the place. Take care it's dark."

It suited Dan. He would never ride on an engine footplate, or clean out a smoke box, or oil a big end, but he was moved by the experience of steam and rails. "Get me up to the coalsssh ssshtage for when the last engine comes in? I want to see it being coaled up."

"We can get yuh anywhere," chirped Wagget. "Where d'yuh Fancy?"

"On the footplate of that engine," queried Dan.

Joe worried a little for Dan's fragile paralysed body and the fact that they were all a bit worse for drink, but it didn't stop them. They carried him and the chair when the chair couldn't be pushed. They positioned his chair against the cab of coal engine 1445 threading Dan through the cab doorway and seating him on the fireman's side box-seat. Then on with his shed tour again and a spin on the manually operated engine turntable. It was like a scene from a silent movie, they secured Dan and his chair to the handrail of the turntable and whisked it around as fast as they could make it spin.

"Yee hah," Dan cried out, playing to the audience of shedmen who'd turned out to cheer him on. The tour was extended to include a visit to the store and the sand furnace, the fitter's shop and numerous engines. Then finally up onto the coal stage to watch the coalman fill the tender of a stabled locomotive. A sudden gust of wind whisked up all the coal dust and covered the group in a black shroud. They all laughed heartily at their predicament as Dan rubbed his eyes clean and broke into a Louis Armstrong routine.

They made there way jovially back to the messroom. "And here's a little wedding present from the lads in the shed," Bill Frobisher leaned over and presented a package to Dan. "We've collected for you and your Lady?"

The homeward trip saw them both a little repentant. Wagget and Hibson had gone their own way and Dan and Joe, both extremely dirty, feeling sick, silly, and vowing never to get drunk again, pressed slowly towards the West's household.

Dan was surprised to find Nancy at his house, "You, Daniel West, you will never be allowed to forget. If you ever come home with a ruined suit and as drunk as coot you'll...., you'll." She couldn't find the right words.

"I'll never forget thisssh night," Dan pleaded. "You should have a go at Joe, he led me on. I didn't know we'd go down to the engine sheds."

But Joe had diplomatically staggered off to his own home only to be scorched by his Mother's condemnation and blasted by his Father.

Nancy calmed and left for her home address, so as not to see Dan on her nuptial day, and a few hours of sleep descended on the West household.

Dan's empty wheelchair waited alongside the bed, while its owner found some relief with the passing of each hour. The appointed wedding time arrived and the families met, maybe for the first time, maybe the last time, but they displayed genuine pleasure and best wishes for the happy couple.

Daniel had dutifully, and not without his eternal spring of humour, washed away the memories of Nancy's scolding the evening before. His bachelor days and suffering was about to end as she arrived by his side before the altar.

She stopped beside his wheelchair and he took her by the hand gently squeezing it. He whispered quietly to her, "You look beautiful my pet, and I love you."

She smiled slightly and cast her eyes down briefly to see his pursed lips send a kiss, happily she returned the almost silent signal. The thought drifted through her mind. 'Diamonds are rough until they are cut and polished. I've got some cutting and polishing to do.'

The Vicar, commenced with the first verbal signals of the wedding service and the course of two lives changed forever.

4

Property of the Nation

"1948's goin' to be new year with a 'ell of a difference," Arthur Wilko asserted loudly. A large group of enginemen had gathered in the messroom shortly after the Christmas break. "We ought to have a celebration."

"Or a march, like they do in France and Italy," added Jack Riby. "The Mere club is sure to be full of regulars."

"What with the nationalisation of the railways coming up," returned Wilko. "That's good news for us all."

"Yuh reckon, Wilko, bet it never 'appens."

"Course it will, it's gone through parliament."

"Na, the good news'll never happen, I mean, it'll just carry on as normal."

The London & North Eastern Railway Company which had been formed in January 1923 was to become part of a newly created British Railways at midnight on 1st January 1948. All the men knew that and all secretly hoped for better times. Many promises made at the polls in response to the sacrifices of the wartime years had already been delivered by the government. Railmen looked forward to more job security, better working conditions and promotion prospects. Other large industries such as the water, gas and electricity companies were being united, modernised and nationalised. Everybody expected more and railwaymen expressed a large part of that expectation.

Revellers would be out in large numbers to see 1947 pass into memory. The year had been a traumatic one. A bleak devastating winter with heavy snows, followed by floods and hurricane winds, food shortages, electricity cuts, rationing and continued conscription had completed a disparate mosaic of dramatic events. People looked forward with new hope.

"We ought to have good time. A party, crackers, food and a bonfire." Alf South joined in the conversation. "Like V.E. day parties. We could join the crowd that gather at Boots' corner."

"I'll be in the Hole in the Wall pub," said Jingo drearily. He was scribbling away at the report desk in the messroom."

"Hope somebody fills up t'hole while you're in it."

Jingo looked around but didn't see who'd uttered the sarcastic retort.

"Sounds like a good idea to me. Not everybody agrees with nationalisation but they'll come to a party. We'll mek it our own celebration party. Have it here after the Tavern closes. In here, in the messroom."

"Can you fix something up Tom? You always get away wi' murder around here."

"Yes Tom, yuh can," said Alf South agreeably.

"Joe, yuh can help, can't yuh?" stated Rob Hibson.

"What about Fifty Bob? Bob Burton. He retires on the New Year's Eve, We can give him a good send off an' all."

The discussion became too fragmented for a decision to emerge but the message that passed by word of mouth told everyone that, 'A.S.L.E.F. are having a drink on New Year's Eve, in the store and the messroom, N.U.R. members are invited.'

Arthur Wilko's fifty-wagon coal train was easing back slowly into number two road. The slight tightening and slackening of the three link iron couplings was the audible indicator of the train's gentle approach. The danger posed by backing the heavy load was well monitored by both the guard and Joe who leaned out of the cab.

"Let her go back, Arthur, still on a green. Steady now, amber, side to side, nearly there. Whoa! Red light." Joe converted the guard's visual hand signals into verbal instructions for his driver who was looking carefully out of the other side. The clash of buffers as the train closed up to the buffer stop told the driver that he'd backed his eight-hundred ton coal train safely into the siding.

A long, active day had preceded their arrival, they were ready for home but the celebrations were calling, indeed, were insisting. Three axle box fires had occurred in their train of privately owned old wagons that depended on grease or fat to lubricate the axle bearings. That had meant a lot of shunting of the failed vehicles for Arthur and Joe on their journey from Gascoinge Wood sidings.

"The shedmaster's here did you say?" Joe asked Arthur as their B16 locomotive number 1445 entered the shed yard and stopped on number one road.

"So I was told when you were turning me into the yard, he's stopping 'till midnight, to bring in the New Year and mark the creation of British Railways." He descended from the cab before Joe and gave instructions. "Tie the engine down Joe, make her fast. I'm going home first for a wash and change."

So unusual was a spontaneous celebration of this nature, that word had spread rapidly throughout the shed and to some in the nearby community. New Years Eve and the following day were not annual occasions that were marked officially by employers, or by the granting of a day away from work. With the spread of the news, a new rumour was abroad that Franker the shedmaster was also to be leaving his post.

"That alright Mr Franker," Tom West asked less boisterously than usual. He was almost subdued. His question to Franker was asked in the tone of someone seeking approval, it related to the messroom that was exceptionally clean and tidy and displayed some drinks and a few cakes and scones set out on plates. The men's own mugs of coffee, tea or cocoa were either waiting on the table, or spread out on an inverted box close to the boiling kettle.

The hiss of a moving locomotive in the shed accompanied by a short pop on the steam whistle as it halted outside the messroom door was a reminder that the shed was still a place of work and labour. The boilersmith was busy washing out a boiler, Jack Mild, the steamraiser, was visiting different engines, lighting them up from dead, or just seeing that those in steam were safe and quiet. The shed fitter and his mate were still working on the Walschaerts valve gear of a B1 engine.

By ten-thirty pm, the men ceased their work and drifted into the messroom. The shedmaster was warmed by the spirit of the occasion. Cards and dominoes made their appearance as the numbers present increased. Tom West arranged for a few bottles and more food to be brought in from his home. A mouth organ was produced and popular musical hall and soldier's songs were played. Slowly the volume developed as more joined in the verses and choruses.

"Your loo paper and comb, Alf." Hibson jested. "You're jolly good on that, ain't yuh."

A short blast on guard's whistle emanated from Tom West. Jack Lambert raised his arms aloft in a attempt to command attention, slowly a kind of order settled on the messroom.

Tom West raised his hands and held them together as if in prayer, not intentionally, but for long enough for Willy Wagget to shout with intended humour. "We are gathered here this evening brothers to do our...."

Tom scowled at Willy and commenced to speak. "We are gath....." A howling laughter accompanied his attempt to start. He stared around and started again, but this time with stronger words. "Everybody shut their mouths," he emphasised. "In proper Yorkshire fashion, shut yuh gobs and listen." He paused. "We really are gathered....."

"Tom, you've got the same record on," Hibson joined in the verbal harassment.

Tom turned to Mr Franker, "See how they've all come to see you, and you thought it was the beer and food didn't you."

Franker nodded, with a feigned expression of displeasure on his face, but it was sufficient to quell the chatter.

"Yes," Tom continued, now with everyone's attention. "At the stroke of Midnight we all become part of British Railways, so we've asked Mr Franker to speak to us to mark the occasion here in Castlebrough. He also has something to tell us of his personal plans. Over you over to Mr Franker."

Franker moved out from behind the table and an expectant hush descended. He laid his trilby on the table.

"It's a mixture of good news and not so good news that I want to tell you. I'll start with the good news first. Just to say that we will soon all be employees of British Railways, let's hope that is going to be for the better. It won't make much difference to you immediately, the railways have been controlled and subsidised by the government since the start of the war. But there'll soon be a big programme of locomotive building getting underway. Half a million new wagons to replace the old privately owned ones. New track being laid. We look like we're set up for a long railway future.

"Yeah, the railways won the war," interrupted John Smithers. "Now they're goin' to win the peace." A cheer of agreement and approval rose then subsided as Franker waited to say some more.

"Now for Fifty Bob, I mean of course, Bob Burton," he turned to Bob engaged him and commenced to pay him credit, listing some of the experiences, achievements and contributions he'd made in his forty-five years as a first class railwayman.

"Your one of the grand old timers, Bob, started on the old North Eastern in 1903. By, you've seen a lot of changes, but always you played a big part in the work of this shed. You've helped with the welfare of the men, the cottage homes, the convalescent home, the mutual improvement classes, and with workers education. Your part has been outstanding."

Mr Franker took Bob Burton's hand and shook it warmly. "Bob, you're one of those men I'm glad I had the pleasure to meet. On behalf of myself, your workmates and the London and North Eastern Railway, I present you with this gift."

Franker handed Bob a boxed gift from the railway company.

"Ha, the good old L.N.E.R., it's a blooming clock," exclaimed Bob.

"You've guessed it! It's a mahogany, free standing pendulum clock. Put it on the mantelpiece and time Mrs Burton while she does all of her housework. But don't you tell her I said so." He paused while the friendly, sometimes cheeky remarks from the gathering were completed.

Bob said a few words himself. "I've never been provided with a watch to time trains by the company, now they've given me a clock to sit and watch the hours go by in my retirement." Laughter and jocular remarks broke out to the accompaniment of light applause.

"Now," Franker paused, "I want to tell young Wade about his good fortune. From next week Joe, you're made up to fireman. Appointed to be fireman to Frank Kettley. You've both been made into a set of men, one of our seventeen sets of men on the shed. I hope you and Frank work together as a team for a long time."

"Good on yuh, Joe."

"Well done kid."

A slight applause broke out but soon settled as the men sensed that Franker still had more to say.

"Lastly, for myself," he paused and drew a large breath. "I'm leaving tomorrow. I'm not likely to come this way again," he paused again briefly. "And tonight," he kept halting as if he didn't know what to say next. "Tonight, from midnight the London and North Eastern Railway ceases to be as such. It may be that Joe becomes the very first new appointee to be notified of promotion on the new unified railway system of England, Wales and Scotland. It looks like I'm going to be the first person to leave. I leave tomorrow on the afternoon train. I have to go a because of sickness."

The hush in the messroom was intense, the men had all had their showdowns with Franker, but to hear of him speak like this was unknown.

"I would like to have spoken to all the shedmen, but, for those not here or on duty running the railway tonight, I will have to ask you to convey my very best wishes to them. Parting from friends is always painful and I'm sorry to be parting from you."

"Parting reminds me of wartime, in the Great War, I was in the trenches in France, and in Salonika. Charlie over there was with me in Salonika, side by side in the trenches. They know what it is to feel a strong kinship that exists between two strangers in the war, strangers who act like brothers when the fear and threat of death is prevalent."

"You look to see if your pal is still alive as the shells fall, you pray harder for him than you do for yourself. You need him, to reassure you, even if there is fear in his eyes, or tears on his face, you need him more than you feel you need yourself."

"That was a long time ago. Since then, many of us, in here, have formed friendships that will be with us for a long time. On this shed there have been good times as well as bad times, sometimes trauma of a terrible kind, like the men I know who have died at work, but always there has been a fine spirit of comradeship here, the finest in all of the places in the North East where I've worked. I'd call it the Northern spirit."

"There's been another war. There's peace and a new start now. But it's time for me to move on. I'll carry with me memories of Castlebrough and all of you, the boilersmiths, the fitter and mate, the steam raisers, coalmen, clerks, engine cleaners, firemen and drivers. Men like young Joe Wade here, I always smile when I think of you, Joe." He looked at Joe. "Eager and keen to be Bob Laker's fireman on the York train. Bob told me how you fared and how you threw your shovel into the firebox, and how you didn't tell anyone."

A round of laughter rumbled through the room.

"This is my farewell letter," he held up a piece of note paper. "I'll put it in the case. To you and all the others who are not here, we've always worked together. I'll think of the men of Castlebrough as long as I live."

Franker bowed his head and after what seemed a like a long pause of silence, a hearty applause broke out. Tom West raised his glass, he and Franker had often been at loggerheads but tonight the hatchet was well and truly buried. "Its nearly midnight," Tom declared, "Let's raise our glasses to Mr Franker....., to Bob Burton....., and to British Railways."

St James' Church bells were heard to herald in the new year. "Happy New Year everybody." Joy and laughter spread contagiously as 1948 dawned and the London and North Eastern Railway became history.

The euphoria began to fade shortly afterwards as one or two of the more tired souls began to drift home. Franker left too, but before he went, he confided in Tom West, speaking of his reason for leaving railway service. He told Tom of the seriousness of an incurable illness which had stuck him down.

"Surely, you don't have to go just because of that," Tom had said, stunned by what he'd just heard. "You'll get better."

Franker had shook his head in response. "They think its too late."

Joe was emotional as he cycled home. The sad news that Tom had quietly circulated about Franker had affected him. For Joe, the night had brought good fortune, but the knowledge that Franker was fighting his last battle cast a heavy mantle over his spirits.

He stopped his cycle on the corner of his street and gazed up into the beauty of the night sky. His thoughts turned to Rachael, of the birth of British Railways, Dan's recent wedding and also of his new responsibilities at work. Then by contrast he recalled his fondest memories of the old London and North Eastern, of Bob Burton and of Shedmaster Franker whose fate was now uncertain.

A distant loco whistle echoed through the still calm of the night, stirring Joe from his reverie. He looked skyward again, at the crystal clear inverted hemisphere, full of brilliant stars and displaying all the wealth and magic found in the Universe.

"Some things," he murmured to himself, "begin when others end."

The End